P9-EJI-369

A VOLUME IN THE
LIFE OF SCIENCE LIBRARY (NO. 23)

CLAUDE BERNARD & THE EXPERIMENTAL METHOD IN MEDICINE

CLAUDE BERNARD *from an original photograph by Pierre Pettit*

CLAUDE BERNARD &

THE EXPERIMENTAL METHOD IN MEDICINE

BY

J. M. D. OLMSTED

Professor of Physiology at the University of California. Membre correspondant de la Société philomathique de Paris. Prix Binoux, Académie des Sciences, 1949.

&

E. HARRIS OLMSTED

HENRY SCHUMAN · NEW YORK

MANUFACTURED IN THE UNITED STATES BY
H. WOLFF

TO

MAURICE GENTY

CONTENTS

PREFACE

The authors welcome the opportunity to contribute a study of their favorite subject to the Life of Science Library. They wish to point out that their manner of collaboration is new. Formerly E. Harris Olmsted has contributed only advice on the philosophical matters which are her own field. For this book she has undertaken the actual writing. The broad outlines of the narrative of the scientific discoveries are the same as those laid down by Professor Olmsted in his earlier biography of Claude Bernard. He has also appraised the new manuscript material released in France since the publication of *Claude Bernard, Physiologist* in 1939. Mrs. Olmsted has made an even fuller use of the Raffalovich letters than that of the earlier book, and has included a few letters of Bernard's boyhood which have not been referred to in an English work before.

The authors wish to acknowledge courtesies from Dr. Léon Binet, Dr. Maurice Caullery, Dr. Jean Marie Le Goff, Dr. John Fulton, Robert Brode, Victor Lenzen, George Sarton, and Mr. Henry Schuman, whose interest in the project has been unflagging. Their special gratitude is offered to Dr. Maurice Genty, Librarian of the Academy of Medicine in Paris, who has maintained their liaison with critical studies of Bernard in France.

E. HARRIS OLMSTED
JAMES M. D. OLMSTED

January, 1952.

CLAUDE
BERNARD &
THE EXPERIMENTAL METHOD IN MEDICINE

I

CLAUDE BERNARD'S RELATION TO THE EXPERIMENTAL METHOD OF MODERN MEDICINE

> *Physiology, which is the science of the laws of life, incontestably deals with the most complex phenomena in nature. It is therefore not astonishing that its advance should be so slow, and its appearance in the ranks of the exact sciences so long delayed.* Report on the Progress and Achievements of Physiology in France.

WHY IS THE NAME OF CLAUDE BERNARD ASSOCIATED WITH the experimental method as applied to medicine? The method is as old as science itself, and its application to medicine, although long delayed, was made through physiology two centuries before Bernard's time by William Harvey in England. In France the experimental method was reinstated for medicine at the opening of the nineteenth century by François Magendie, under whom Bernard was proud to have served his apprenticeship as a physiologist. Many of Bernard's contemporaries, especially in Germany, were using the experimental procedure with increasing success.

In the first place, the sum of Bernard's achievements

finally silenced skepticism about the power of experiment to draw from nature the secrets of the living organism. His work closed a period in the history of medicine. Considered singly, none of his discoveries was of the sort which transforms the whole scene overnight. Yet each brought to light some fundamental truth of organic function; and the whole of his accomplishment in the twenty years of his greatest activity, 1839 to 1859, did transform the scene and make him the foremost physiologist of his time.

In the second place, after his most intensive period of work, Bernard paused to harvest his experience in another way. He composed a description of the experimental method as applied to physiology, and illustrated it by his own researches. His most famous book, *Introduction à l'étude de la médecine expérimentale (Introduction to the Study of Experimental Medicine),*[1] begins with an analysis of the principles of physiological investigation, and ends with simple, vivid narratives of key episodes in his most important discoveries. We see the mind of a great scientist at work. After eighty-five years it is still read by physiologists with the same sort of appreciation as was expressed by Bernard's slightly younger contemporary, Louis Pasteur.

Pasteur's son-in-law and biographer, René Vallery-Radot, says that when Pasteur spoke of the *Introduction* he did so as if he were not a rival, but a pupil of Bernard. Pasteur's own career shows how complete a reversal had

[1] The *Introduction,* except for a volume of early technical lectures and a surgical handbook, is the only work of Bernard translated into English. This translation by Henry Copley Greene carries a preface by Lawrence J. Henderson (Henry Schuman, 1949), whose physiological research was an elaborate development of the doctrine of organic function enunciated by Bernard. The preface has acquired a certain fame of its own.

occurred since Magendie opened his campaign against biological indeterminism, maintaining that the phenomena of life were as scientifically dependable as physical or chemical phenomena. Pasteur was a chemist, who, by his discovery of the living organisms which cause many diseases, opened up a whole new field of medicine, bacteriology, without himself ever having practiced medicine, or, indeed, even having taken a medical degree. The vindication of the experimental method for medicine had been accomplished within the borders of France in the space of about two generations, Magendie's and Bernard's.

Bernard himself, although he fulfilled the requirements for his medical degree, never practiced medicine, devoting his whole life to experimental physiology. Nevertheless, his work was done with an eye to the curing of disease. He vigorously opposed the substitution of "experimental physiology" for medicine in the title of his chair at the College of France. In his last decade he emphasized a broader view of the subject matter of his science and became, officially, a general, as well as a medical, physiologist. Yet the manuscript notes[2] for the book to which he always intended the famous *Introduction* to be merely an introduction show that what he regarded as his life work was the application to medicine of the general principles of scientific method. His earlier discoveries were concerned with the functions of particular bodily organs, the pancreas and the liver; but as his work progressed, it gave greater prominence to the unified activity of the whole body. His conception of the blood as furnishing an internal environment which mediates between living tissues and the external environment is a striking illustration of this tendency.

[2] Edited by Leon Delhoume and published posthumously in France in 1947 as *Principes de médecine expérimentale (Principles of Experimental Medicine)*.

In his *Introduction* Bernard offered a criterion for measuring the importance of scientific discoveries:

> We usually give the name of discovery to recognition of a new fact: but I think that the idea connected with the discovered fact is what really constitutes the discovery. Facts are neither great nor small in themselves. A great discovery is a fact whose appearance in science gives rise to ideas shedding a bright light which dispels many obscurities and shows us new paths. There are other facts which, although new, teach us but little; they are therefore small discoveries. Finally, there are new facts which, although well observed, mean nothing to anyone; they remain, for the time being, detached and sterile in science; they are what we may call crude or raw facts.

Bernard would have been the first to agree that the studies of Pasteur which revealed the existence of microorganisms constituted a great discovery. His later critical attitude to Pasteur's theoretical view of fermentation did not affect his appreciation of the discovery which launched the new science of bacteriology. No single experimental idea of Bernard's had results quite so spectacular. Perhaps the closest parallel is to be found in the wide ramifications of endocrinology, which may be traced to his introduction of the concept of internal secretion. Each of his four chief discoveries had a wide reference to the principles of organic function, and many of his isolated observations were fertile for later investigators. In a more general way, through his concept of the nature of the living organism, particularly as expressed in his doctrine of the internal environment, his influence upon medical investigation has been at least as dynamic as that of Pasteur. It is, moreover, an influence which shows fewer signs of having run its full course.

2

FRENCH COUNTRY BOY (1813–1834)

It is half-past four in the morning, a little before my usual hour, to be sure, . . . but where am I? I am at Saint-Julien, I open my window, I see the garden: the rising sun barely penetrates the dense leaves of two big mulberry trees close to my window; I hear the steady chirp of the figpeckers. . . . I see the cooing pigeons on the edge of the roof . . . ah! How nice it is! Letter to Benoit Blanc, August, 1834.

THERE HAVE BEEN MANY FAMILIES IN FRANCE IN WHICH membership in the medical profession was a tradition passed from one generation to the next. Magendie's father was a physician; Laennec accompanied to the wars an uncle who served as an army surgeon during the Revolution. But the family into which Claude Bernard was born had no such associations. For as many generations as could be remembered, most of its members had been vinegrowers among the hills rising from the valley of the Rhone.

Pierre Jean François Bernard, twenty-two, married Jeanne Saulnier, nineteen, in the autumn of 1807. The youngest of four sons, Pierre had no land but two vineyards on Chatenay hill overlooking the village of Saint-Julien-en-Beaujolais were part of Jeanne's dowry. The young couple came to live in a farmhouse on Chatenay which belonged to Jeanne's mother.

The farmhouse on the hilltop opened upon a walled courtyard, and ignored the eastward view across the broad valley of the Saône, tributary to the Rhone, toward Mont Blanc, dim in the distance. A high wall with tile coping and a gateway ran on the north side of the yard from the house to an older rough stone building with a square tower crowned by a pointed roof, which served as a pigeon loft. Sheds over the wine cellars bounded the east side of the yard, and on the south the wall had a wide opening, looking out upon vine-clad slopes. The yearly vintage came into the courtyard by the wide gate and the wine, when it was sold, went out by the gate in the opposite wall to the road. One end of the farmhouse was used as a barn; the principal downstairs room was low-ceilinged, with blackened beams. The flat stone above the fireplace had roughly incised on it the date 1801 and the initials *e.s.,* those of Étienne Saulnier, Jeanne's father.

A heavy table, straw-seated chairs, cupboards, and a chest of drawers were the chief furnishings, along with the brick stove on which the soup was prepared over charcoal. In the upstairs room stood a wide Empire bed with bronze eagles on its posts. Furniture decorated in this style had come into fashion in honor of the Emperor Napoleon. It was in this bed that a son, the first child of Pierre and Jeanne Bernard, was born in the sixth year of their marriage.

Early in the morning of July 12, 1813, Pierre Bernard went down the hill to the village of Saint-Julien to register the birth which had occurred between three and four o'clock during the night. The mayor's office, where this record may still be read, was in the same building as the village school. Around the square were a few other modest houses, the presbytery, the church, and two huge plane trees screening the entrance to the château. In the center was the well.

When the baby was six days old, he was baptized by the parish priest, receiving the second Christian name of his paternal grandfather, Pierre Claude Bernard, who came from Arnas, not far away, to act as godfather. Jeanne Bernard's family was represented by her great-aunt, Marguerite Baloffet, of whom nothing is remembered except that she had never learned to write and therefore could not sign the baptismal certificate. The two witnesses were friends of Pierre Bernard and vinegrowers like himself.

Little Claude's first view of the outside world, when he was old enough to play at the farmhouse door, was of a pleasant enclosed space, with one or two old trees, a well, and the pigeons flying back and forth to the corner tower. A little later he would discover the orchard beyond the barn, and outside the wider gate, stretching as far as the eye could see, acres of vineyards.

The collapse of Napoleon's empire had begun in the autumn of the year of Claude's birth and was complete before he was two years old. The bronze eagles, now a politically unpopular decoration, were removed from the posts of the wide bed. The Bernard family became involved in the economic consequences of the Emperor's downfall. Pierre Bernard had taken a partner who, hoping for higher profits by eliminating the usual brokers, went into the wine business in Paris. The venture failed. Although part of the vineyards which Pierre Bernard had acquired through his wife were sold, there were still debts left unpaid. The family was enlarged by the birth of a daughter. Bernard tried to recoup his losses by planting mulberry trees for the culture of silkworms, but the plan proved impractical. Finally he tried to add to his income by acting as schoolmaster. He used his own house as a classroom, and the children of the neighborhood were sent to him to receive elementary instruction in reading, writing, geography, and arithmetic.

Perhaps because Pierre Bernard was well educated for a French villager, he wished his son to go further than he had himself. Or perhaps Jeanne cherished the characteristic wish of pious French peasant women that her son become a priest. We know that Claude Bernard was more strongly attached to his mother than to his rather unsuccessful father, for friends of his later years often heard him speak affectionately of his mother, but could remember no mention of his father.

When Claude was eight years old, he was sent to the house of a local priest, Père Bourgaud, to learn Latin. When he was about eleven, Père Bédouin, who was in charge of the parish at Saint-Julien, "attracted by his serious manner," not only gave him instruction in Latin, but arranged to have him assist at mass, hoping, no doubt, that the boy would choose to enter the service of the Church. Two other clerics, Abbés des Garets and Desarbes, also became interested in Claude, and recommended his admission to the Jesuit college in the small industrial town of Villefranche, about five miles away. At that time the college occupied a part of the ancient Convent of the Visitation, a bleak, uninviting building which is still standing. There Claude was taught more Latin, a little Greek, French literature, arithmetic, and geometry. Such subjects as physics, chemistry, or biology had no place in the curriculum.

Some of the boy's school books have been preserved at the farmhouse, now a memorial museum, among them a French-Latin dictionary, a dictionary of classical antiquities, a history of Greece, and a French grammar. A volume of Tacitus looks quite new, and a copy of Cicero's oration *Pro Milone* also shows no wear. There is no Horace but in later life Bernard proved his familiarity with this poet by casual references and quotations in his letters. He had a boyish trick of inscribing his books in Greek script, "Bernard, Claude, Saint-Julien, Rhône," with the date, 1829. Forty-five years later, as an excuse for what he deemed lack of "style" in his handwriting, he recalled his interest in "all kinds of scripts," and his facility in block printing.

When he was seventeen, on the continued recommendation of the Abbé des Garets, and also of the Abbé Donnet, curé at Villefranche and later archbishop of Bordeaux, he was admitted as a student "in philosophy" at the College of Thoissey (Ain). This was a seventeenth-century foundation, the gift of Mlle. de Montpensier, niece of Louis XIII, and secondary education there was free. The college was about twenty miles north of Villefranche, so that it was no longer possible for Claude to live at home. It is unlikely that he was taught any science even here. The parlor of the college for many years displayed a manuscript of seventy-two pages submitted for a prize by Bernard under the title "Notes on Miniature Painting," with the motto, "Always follow nature, for she is the best model."

As a boy Claude seems to have impressed only a few priests who thought his pensive and serious manner might indicate a vocation for the church. Schoolmates recalled him as rather unfriendly and not very clever. He did not join in the school games, but seemed aloof and dreamy. His teachers considered him an ordinary student, and one in particular commented that he never liked to read, because, as the boy explained, it seemed a waste of valuable time.

Perhaps the available reading matter was not very alluring. Among the fresh-looking school books preserved at the farmhouse there is a battered copy of the eighteenth-century French translation of John Barclay's *Argenis,* which in its time started a fashion for historical romances. Oddly enough, there occur in this book, in connection with accounts of battle wounds, spirited criticisms of the ignorance of physicians and their preoccupation with fees. There is a tradition that when Claude came to what is called in French "the age of reason" (perhaps the translation into contemporary speech would be "the 'teen age"), he had a room of his own under the pigeon tower. Perhaps it was there that he read romances. At all events, it is clear that the old-fashioned classical discipline of the church schools gave the boy little opportunity to display his natural talents, however well it may have served to awaken and preserve his vigorous intelligence.

When Claude was eighteen, the family could not afford to carry his education any further. In January, 1832, he was taken on as an apprentice in the shop of a pharmacist, Louis Joseph Marie Millet, on the main street of Vaise, a suburb of Lyons on the west bank of the Saône, a little more than twenty miles south of Saint-Julien. Probably he or his family hoped he might get a professional foothold here. Pharmacist shops often serve the small towns of France as medical centers, and the proprietors have some local dignity.

Claude's apprenticeship included sweeping the pavement, rinsing bottles, and running errands. From time to time he was allowed to serve customers, with his employer looking on, and he was cautiously initiated into the art of preparing pills and powders. His youthful pride suffered. Years afterward he recalled that when he heard the hoofbeats announcing the arrival of the stagecoach from Villefranche, he would withdraw into the darkest corner of the shop to avoid the stares or jokes of acquaintances. When he was older, if he referred to this period of his life at all, he was apt to take a humorous tone. He liked to amuse his scientific colleagues by showing them how neatly he could arrange a fluting of paper around corks and telling them where he had learned it. After a demonstration of elegant block lettering, he would remark that it was the result of practice in labeling medicine bottles. He confided to the journalist Sarcey, forty years after the event: "I never felt keener pleasure than the day I first made shoe blacking. I was master of a trade, I knew how to do something, I was a man."

As errand boy he regularly visited a veterinary school nearby, to deliver drugs for the sick animals. The pharmacist was surprised at Claude's interest in what went on in this institution, which had a certain celebrity as the first of its kind in Europe. The activities of the veterinarians presented something of a contrast to life at the pharmacy, which Claude described in a letter as "bounded by four walls and three hundred bottles."

His inclination to be critical of the trade he was learning increased when he found out how *la thériaque,* a favorite remedy with a long and honorable pharmaceutical history, was prepared in the shop. Scrapings of mixing dishes and the dregs of bottles were never thrown away, but saved to make *la thériaque*. The remedy seemed to be just as effective when made of accidental left-overs as when properly compounded of all sixty of the traditional ingredients. Since the drugs were dissolved in honey and wine, it is not too hard to understand why the customers approved of the mixture. Claude Bernard, however, began to doubt whether much was really known about the efficacy of drugs.

The apprentice of those days was not allowed much free time, but "Monsieur Claude" (this was the form of address which the pharmacist finally chose for his assistant) was at liberty to go out into the town by himself one night a month. The Lyons of 1832, like Paris, of which it was the provincial rival, had not yet assumed the modern aspect which wide boulevards now give it. It was approached from Vaise over a narrow stone bridge built in the sixteenth century, and many of its streets followed a tortuous medieval course. Yet it had fashionable shops, promenades, public baths, cafés, and two theaters, one putting on vaudeville and musical comedy, the other the romantic dramas of the period. Claude was attracted by the theaters. He spent his free evenings in them and before the year was out wrote and had staged a vaudeville sketch of his own, called *La Rose du Rhône*.

He shared a room at the pharmacy with another apprentice, Benoit Blanc, who had been his schoolfellow at Villefranche. Blanc was sound asleep one night when a retort over his head exploded and drenched him with some pharmaceutical fluid (no strict line being drawn between laboratory and bedroom accommodations). His astonishment increased when he saw Bernard still up and at work under the lamp in his bare feet. He was putting the last touches on his play. Blanc afterward related that he was not allowed to go to sleep again until the whole work had been read to him, and at the end he was very nearly as enthusiastic as the author. Nothing remains of this production except its name and the statement in one of Bernard's letters, written much later, that he received about one hundred francs for it.

With this success behind him, Bernard decided to try his hand at historical drama. In 1832 a Paris company had appeared at the Grand Théâtre of Lyons in plays by Dumas and Victor Hugo, and also in two plays derived from Shakespeare. Bernard probably saw these performances. The pharmacist observed a lack of attention to business in his apprentice and wrote to Bernard's father, complaining that "Monsieur Claude" had lost interest in pharmacy, and asking to be relieved of further responsibility for an apprentice who was also a playwright. Claude himself wrote to his father that he could not make up his mind, "when I am only nineteen, . . ." to spend the rest of his life folding up little squares of paper.

He was at home in Saint-Julien in January, 1833, and on the 25th wrote to Benoit Blanc, still in Vaise:

> The day draws near, and I am taking great steps toward the end I have in view. I am busy passing my examinations, and not without work, as you may imagine, my poor Pierre. I am writing to you in great haste; otherwise I should hold forth at length to you and the friends we share. Today I can only prove that I am still alive, lest you think me dead or frozen. . . . I shall write to you soon, at the first opportunity, about a tale; oh! another of those tales. You shall see, I promise, and I shall keep my word. In the meantime, please ask our friends to come to see me in Saint-Julien. I am on the lookout for you, and shall be very grateful.
>
> Tell Chrétien and Lambert that I often think affectionately of them. . . .
>
> My little Pierre, once more I send my love.

The tone of this letter amends the accepted tradition that Bernard was reserved and solitary in his youth. He was obviously on confidential and affectionate terms with Benoit Blanc, although there is a touch of patronage in the fanciful epithets by which he addresses his friend (other letters prove that he almost always substituted for Benoit's own name "my Pierre," "my Ronne," or "marquis de la Ronne"). Chrétien and Lambert (a youth with a wooden arm) were law students, and two other favorite comrades were nicknamed Grisgi (a young priest) and Chonchon. The four early letters of Bernard preserved by the Blanc family of Villefranche show that, during the next two years, spent mostly in Saint-Julien, he went to country fairs and dances with these young men, sometimes making an "unforeseen impression" on the local beauties, or joined them in card games or the good wine of Beaujolais under a rural trellis on Sunday afternoons.

The "examinations" of the letter (perhaps the *baccalauréats* which would admit him to university studies) were presumably passed. We hear no more of them. On July 7, 1833, Bernard wrote again to Benoit Blanc. He had just recovered from two weeks of illness, which the local doctor, taking a pinch of snuff, had solemnly diagnosed as "an intestinal irritation," prescribing potions, mustard plasters, and "all the terrors" of the pharmacy. The symptoms were frightful headaches and "writhing" stomach pains. Barely on his feet, Bernard was eager to communicate his latest plans:

> Yes, my Pierre, my Ronne, . . . in two weeks with no postponement, there will be a spree, a real spree, I shall tell Chonchon and he must come, and bring Grisgi and Jegefet. We shall spend one more happy day together, and as we uncork the champagne we shall sing:
>
> *Life's stream shall bear*
> *Us on, my friends,*
> *Without a care.* (twice, three times)
>
> I am solitary in my Saint-Julien, and I could not endure it very long, but in two weeks, away to Paris. Ah! Paris, Paris, there lies my hope, yes, there is nothing to match Paris.

He had after all to endure Saint-Julien for another year and five months. The apprenticeship with Millet was formally ended July 30, and Bernard wrote to Blanc: "Write me if you have a friend, if you are content with him, but I warrant you will never have one to match me. Tell me what memories I have left behind, give me news of our *patrona atque patronus,* if I am not yet quite forgotten."

Something happened to postpone the departure for Paris, and Bernard occupied himself with the country pursuits of hunting, fishing, and long walks, "fattening myself, while I wait upon my future destiny." It is likely also that he worked on the play which he had begun in Lyons.

His subject called for detailed knowledge of the history of early thirteenth-century France. His hero, for whom the play was named, was Arthur of Brittany, the same young prince whom English readers know from Shakespeare's tragedy, *King John.* The only scene in Bernard's play which resembles a scene in Shakespeare's is the one in which the jailer is persuaded by Arthur's pleading not to obey King John's order to burn out the boy's eyes. The parallel is not close in detail, even if we consider that Bernard is writing prose and Shakespeare poetry. Bernard may have intended to rewrite *King John* from the French point of view. The only bit of evidence which suggests that he may have known something about the English poet's historical plays is the fact that *La Jeunesse de Henri V,* a dramatization of the career of the Black Prince derived from Shakespeare's *Henry IV* and *Henry V,* was played in Lyons during 1832, while Bernard was there to see it.

It is equally possible that he had learned at school something of the unhappy career of young Arthur of Brittany, which may have appealed to him as a symbol of the struggle of noble youth against adversity. He could in a sense identify himself with his hero. Every scene in the play is written around the idealism, courage, and tender heart of Arthur, helpless in a very wicked world. Bernard himself has told us nothing about the circumstances in which the play was written. He said only that he had at first intended to write a tragedy in verse, but found his "spirit stubborn in the composition of verses."

In August, 1834, Bernard wrote once more to Blanc: "Perhaps you thought that I was in Paris, pounding the pavements, hurrying, breaking my neck and living an unfamiliar life, well, you're wrong, I am in Saint-Julien, I go my own pace, and live the old life."

But he was now confident that delays were at an end. The vintage promised well, and he would accompany Chrétien and Lambert when they returned to Paris for their next term. He was armed with a letter of introduction to Vatout, librarian of Louis Philippe, provided by a kind lady in Villefranche who hoped he would be of use to a young playwright. He had also a certificate of good character from the pharmacist Millet, dated April 19, 1834, to the effect that "M. Claude Bernard . . . aged twenty-one years, entered my employ in the capacity of apprentice, January 1, 1832, and left it July 30, 1833, and during these eighteen months he served with honor and fidelity." Millet bore no malice, but he had nothing to say about the gifts of his apprentice as a pharmacist. He was better suited with Benoit Blanc, whom Bernard was now trying to persuade to come to Paris with him. In November, 1834, when the vintage was over, Bernard went to Lyons, and from there at last took the stagecoach for Paris, presumably in the company of Chrétien and Lambert.

3

MEDICAL STUDENT IN PARIS (1834–1843)

Ah! my Ronne, you must come to Paris. . . . You are young, you can be free and work hard. Letter to Benoit Blanc, August, 1834.

A TALL, GRAVE, RATHER AWKWARD YOUNG MAN, IN HIS twenty-first year, Claude Bernard came to Paris in the early, "liberal" years of the reign of Louis Philippe. He carried his letter of introduction to the king's librarian, who, in turn, gave him one to the professor of French poetry at the Sorbonne, Saint-Marc Girardin. Girardin consented to read *Arthur of Brittany* and even made some annotations on the manuscript, but his verdict disappointed the author's hopes. He thought Bernard lacked the "temperament of a dramatist." He must have been sympathetic enough to understand that this opinion might be a serious blow, for he talked with the young man and found out about his experience in the pharmacy in Lyons. He suggested that Bernard remain in Paris and study medicine. A profession and a means of livelihood might also provide leisure for literary experiments.

Girardin obviously felt that the young man who had written *Arthur of Brittany* on the strength of half a dozen visits to the theater should not be sent home to cultivate vines or to carry on small transactions over a counter in a pharmacist's shop. His advice may not have meant that he thought Bernard without literary talent, but that he believed it unwise for the young man to expect a livelihood from writing plays. The construction of *Arthur of Brittany* shows Bernard's possession of a fundamental literary gift, the power to conceive and carry out a complicated plan. As Renan recognized, "there is logic in a five-act drama." There is also imagination in Bernard's presentation of his characters, who emerge from their historical background as quite real, if not very complicated, people. A number of passages bear witness to delicacy of feeling and natural eloquence. Reading the play today, one learns a good deal about the thoughtful and sensitive young man who wrote it.

Girardin's judgment of the play was supported by that of the actor Ligier, who had played many leading roles in the dramas of Dumas and Hugo. Vatout arranged to have *Arthur of Brittany* submitted also to him. When Ligier rejected the play, Bernard accepted the situation, and putting his manuscript carefully away (he preserved it among his private papers all his life), enrolled in the Medical School. Even if his play had not launched him on a theatrical career, it had brought him to Paris.

Student life in the Latin Quarter of 1834 was free and independent, unsheltered either by a modern, international *Cité Universitaire* or by the free hostels of the Middle Ages. The poorer students lived in unheated attics, and supplemented meals in the humbler restaurants with bread and cheese consumed in solitude. Bernard entered this world under the protection of his friends Chrétien and Lambert. He seems to have received almost no financial aid from his father, but the economies of his mother perhaps saved him from the really bitter poverty endured by many of the students. Baskets of pears and similar provisions were sent to him in Paris from Saint-Julien. His really very good secondary education enabled him to obtain a part-time post as teacher of natural history in a girls' school, where his fellow medical students, Ernest Charles Lasègue and Casimir Davaine, who were to be his lifelong friends, also taught. The subjects of his first year in medical school were physics, chemistry, and natural history, and he probably handed on his knowledge of the latter subject in an elementary form almost as soon as he acquired it.

In his second year he began anatomy and physiology, taught more or less together at that time. It was in the study of anatomy that he first began to find himself. He had clever hands and became very skillful in dissection; but he was probably more interested in observing structures and their relationships than in the required memorizing of their Latin names, for he was not regarded as an exceptional student by his first instructors, or by students attending the same courses. In later years his classmates described him as reserved and awkward, perhaps lazy. His teachers noticed his inattentiveness at lectures, probably a result of the tendency to scornful skepticism that he had already displayed in his criticism of the methods of the pharmacy and the diagnostic powers of his country doctor. He nevertheless became extern in 1836, at the end of the usual period of two years of preclinical courses.

The two and one-half years of his externship were spent partly in the grisly dissecting rooms and partly in the hospitals. He left no account of the nightmare scenes prevailing in the former, but his contemporaries corroborate one another in describing the confusion of dispersed limbs and grimacing heads, the blood underfoot, the revolting odors, the sparrows disputing over scraps of lung, rats gnawing vertebrae in a corner.

The perils of the hospital wards were of a different sort.

Bernard promptly fell in love with a young girl hospitalized for treatment of her eyes. He wrote to Benoit Blanc, now established in his own pharmacy in Villefranche:

> I had made my plans beforehand, I had shaved in the morning, blacked my boots, put on my blue beret, and buttoned my frock coat. I went up to her bed, she was more charming than ever, she was reading Walter Scott. I asked her how she was, she replied with the grace and sweetness of an angel. . . . I don't know what will come of it . . . the students have such a bad reputation. What may she not see in the depths of my heart.

The end of the story was not put into writing. When Bernard wrote again to his friend he could say only : "I think I am destined never to be happy in love. I shall tell you about it some other time, when I see you at the vintage."

The vintage always brought Bernard home to Saint-Julien. When he was fifty-seven and thought that the outbreak of the War of 1870-1871 would prevent him from leaving Paris as usual in September, he wrote: "This is the first time in my life that anything has happened to prevent my being on hand for the vintage in my own countryside." He no doubt made himself useful at this season while he was young and strong, but he also thought Saint-Julien was at its best in September and October. To a friend who proposed to visit him there in the spring he wrote: "If you come now on your way back to Paris, I insist that you give me your word to come again for the vintage. I want you to see my countryside when it is beautiful and it is at vintage time that it is most alive and shows its real character."

The goal of the externship was really the competitive examination for the relatively few internships. Even today a rather small number of French medical students gets the intensive clinical experience which an internship in one of the hospitals of Paris provides. The goal of an extern was ordinarily limited to learning by heart answers to certain questions, so as to be able to repeat them in a strictly limited time, giving concise accounts of the researches of other people, and making sure of certain details which have no real but only a formal importance. A favorite device was a mutual coaching club, where the students exchanged résumés of texts and publications and tested one another on the subject matter of lectures. Significantly, there is no record of Bernard having belonged to one of these groups. He was disinclined to go with the crowd, although he had already made acquaintances in Paris which later ripened into firm friendships.

While still an extern he discovered François Magendie, the pioneer who brought physiology in France back to the experimental method in which it had been established by Harvey in England. Magendie grew up in the challenging intellectual atmosphere of the French Revolution. He expressed his disagreement with the indeterminist views of the great anatomist Xavier Bichat at the very beginning of his career. He was bold enough to say that he would like to be the Newton of physiology and place that science on the same sure footing as physics and chemistry. In his successful advocacy of the experimental method he came close to realizing his ambition. He was a practicing physician all his life, but his reputation rested on his research in physiology. His extensive experiments upon animals resulted in important discoveries, especially that of the different functions of the two separate roots of the spinal nerves. The dorsal root, he found, was connected with feeling, the ventral with movement.

The lectures on the nervous system which Magendie was giving at the College of France from December,

1838, to June, 1839, were not compulsory, or perhaps even recommended, for students preparing for the examination through which internships were awarded. But they were of great interest to Bernard, who was beginning to see that anatomy, or the study of form, was only a first step toward knowledge of function in living animals. He was also discovering that his skill in dissection was a valuable technique in physiology. The earliest reference to Bernard in print occurs in Magendie's published lecture of May 29, 1839:

> I have asked M. Bernard, a young anatomist very skillful in delicate dissections, to prepare the facial nerve in a rabbit. Here is the preparation; you are about to see that the dissection will explain to us the fact which we found so puzzling, and that in this case as in many others, it will be a valuable aid in experimental physiology.

At the end of a lecture two days later, another preparation which had been "most carefully dissected by M. Bernard" was exhibited, this time to show that no matter how perfect the dissection, the function of a nerve cannot be established by tracing its path, but must be put to the test of experiment.

It was a very good time to have encountered Magendie. He was at his best in dealing with the nervous system and exhibiting the spectacular results to be obtained by nerve cutting or removal of parts of the brain. An impression of his lecture style may be gained by following the adventures of a duck which he introduced to his class on February 27, 1839:

> We shall take advantage of the few minutes we have left to remove the cerebral lobes of a duck. . . .
>
> I am removing by a stroke of the scalpel the top of the skull, then with the handle of the instrument I scrape

away the lobes of the brain. . . . You see that more skill than time is needed. . . . I draw the skin together again to protect what is left in the skull from injury or foreign bodies.

It is extraordinary how little harm this experiment does to these birds. A duck with its head practically empty does not differ in its gait and behavior from a duck with the brain intact. You have the living proof before your eyes.

The bird will be under observation, and you shall have a report on it.

Magendie continued on March 6:

You have not forgotten the experiment which we performed a week ago on a duck from which the cerebral lobes were entirely removed. I wanted to see how long the animal could live in this condition, and especially if it would preserve the faculty of feeding itself. . . .

As I had foreseen, its general health showed no effects of the removal of the cerebral lobes. When its first surprise was over, it resumed its habits and its promenades; only it seemed less inclined to movement. I cannot say that its sight was entirely destroyed; for it looked for and easily found its water trough, and the plate for its grain. It likes to go paddling as usual, and to judge from the amount of food it consumes, it eats with pleasure and appetite. . . . Usually animals deprived of the cerebral lobes seem to lose the instinct to feed, and forcible feeding is necessary to prevent their dying of starvation.

I want you to notice a "tic" which the duck has acquired since the operation. It constantly shakes its head from side to side, as if making negative gestures. I do not mean that it is inclined to disapprove of something or other; but the fact is that if one could imagine an intention to blame on the part of the bird, it could not show it in a more expressive manner.

> . . . One may ask oneself if there are not in the brain certain parts which particularly preside over the acts by which negation is manifested. When we see certain parts of the brain connected with forward movement, others with backward movement, others with rotatory movement in this or that direction, would it be surprising if the faculty of turning the head in certain directions were subject to similar cerebral influences?

On March 13, Magendie announced the death of the duck, and said it had disappointed his expectations by surviving the operation for only three weeks. He had hoped it might live a month. It had seemed happy, flapped its wings, gone swimming, and indulged from time to time in a quack, until a few days before its death.

It is not difficult to imagine that the more original minds among the medical students would be attracted to Magendie's lectures where everything was so wide open to speculation, and the more conventional in equal degree repelled. It is worth noticing that he began the experiment to settle the question of how long birds could survive when deprived of the cerebral lobes, but became interested in the unforeseen development of a peculiar head movement. This pattern of always watching for unexpected developments in experiments on living material was to reappear more significantly in Bernard's future independent work. It was the first great lesson in the technique of physiological experimentation taught him by Magendie.

The lectures at the College of France in the spring of 1839 grew even more exciting when the lecture room became the scene of what at the moment seemed a major discovery, with an accompanying controversy as to who was the true discoverer.

Magendie, of course, included in his lectures an account of his discovery in 1822 that the dorsal roots of the spinal nerves were associated with feeling and the ventral roots with movement. He also mentioned Charles Bell's claim to have anticipated this discovery. Magendie demonstrated before his class his method of proving the functions of the two roots by cutting them, and so abolishing the functions, an operation demanding great technical skill. He also undertook to demonstrate, by means of pinching or pricking, that stimulation of the dorsal roots caused the animal acute pain, while stimulation of the ventral roots caused none, or very little. In the course of this demonstration it was found that stimulation of the ventral roots, contrary to expectation, did cause pain.

Magendie had pointed out at the beginning of the course that unexpected results must be given the same importance as expected ones. A young Dr. Longet, interested in experimental physiology, acted as a sort of gadfly to the professor by raising difficulties whenever he could. He intervened in the demonstration and pinched a ventral root, of which the corresponding dorsal root was cut, showing that in this case no pain resulted. Before the next lecture, Magendie had devised a more convincing experiment, *i.e.,* cutting the ventral root and pinching in turn both cut ends to show that the sensitivity of the ventral root did not come from its fibers in the cord, but was in some way connected with the sensitivity of the dorsal root. There was a hot dispute in the Academies of Science and of Medicine as to whether Magendie or François Achille Longet had really discovered this new phenomenon of "recurrent sensitivity." Confusion was worse confounded when neither Magendie nor Longet could repeat their experiments demonstrating sensitivity in the ventral roots.

Claude Bernard was an extremely interested witness of

the whole affair. As he said later: "I was witness to the facts. . . . I saw the preparations at close range; I even touched them." It must have been to this time that Bernard's recollections of Magendie's first laboratory went back, for in 1840 the new one, the first in Europe especially designed for physiological investigations, was installed at the College of France for Magendie's personal use. Bernard described the old laboratory as "a sort of small closet where we two could scarcely fit ourselves in," and this description implies that Bernard had done some work for Magendie as a voluntary assistant as early as 1839. The beautiful dissections of the facial nerve of the rabbit which he contributed to illustrate Magendie's investigations of the three branches of this nerve toward the end of the 1839 lectures were probably done in the "closet." The young Bernard must have felt that he was serving in the very front line of the battle of science.

In the meantime he was preparing for the examination for the internship. He was examined in December, 1839, and passed, but by a rather narrow margin, ranking twenty-sixth of the twenty-nine accepted candidates. It is very likely that the time given to Magendie's laboratory, although well spent from the point of view of a would-be physiologist, was ill spent as preparation for the formal medical examination.

Medical students accepted their appointments as interns in the Paris hospitals on condition that they would not graduate in medicine until their term of four years was completed. A series of five examinations had to be passed at intervals of several months during these years. They were, in the order in which they were taken, anatomy and physiology, pathology and nosology, materia medica and pharmacology, hygiene and legal medicine, and clinical medicine. Bernard apparently took these in his stride, as he never made any later reference to them.

As intern Bernard was not immediately attached to the service of Magendie at the Hôtel-Dieu, but served first under two surgeons, Velpeau at the Charité and Maisonneuve at the Hôtel-Dieu. At the Salpetrière he was attached to Falret, who had published a treatise on hypochondria and suicide in 1822. In his only direct reference to his internship at the Salpetrière in 1840, Bernard mentioned the surgeon Manec, describing operations involving the resection of nerves after the removal of tumors thirty years after he had witnessed them. Although he did not serve him as intern, he seems to have attended the scientifically minded Pierre François Olive Rayer at the Charité, where he observed many diabetic cases.

In the second year of his internship he came under Magendie at the Hôtel-Dieu and met an unexpected rebuff. The elderly physician was habitually abrupt and rude in his dealings with the medical students. The hospital was the real battleground between the old medicine and the new, and Magendie liked to emphasize his scientific principles and his medical skepticism by sarcasm. The round of visits to the patients in Magendie's ward, Saint-Monique, began at daybreak. Magendie was punctual and insisted on that virtue in others. After roll call, the professor, followed by other physicians, interns, and externs, passed from bed to bed, questioning and examining the patients. His chief object seemed to be to find fault with whatever treatment his colleagues or subordinates had recommended. As one student put it, "his lip seemed permanently curled in scorn."

Claude Bernard, who already regarded himself as a partisan of physiology and remembered vividly his participation in the course of 1839, probably hoped to be treated differently from the other students, but Magendie made no exception in his favor. We know that Bernard had a certain sense of his own dignity (something which made the pharmacist Millet refer to him at nineteen as "Monsieur Claude") and Magendie's bad manners must have been especially offensive to him. In moments of depression he thought he would wait only until he had his medical degree and then go back to Saint-Julien as the village doctor. He apparently took Dr. Rayer, whom he had met at the Charité, into his confidence. That physician, a friend and scientific associate of Magendie, ventured to say a few words to the distinguished physiologist about the scientific interests of the young intern at the Hôtel-Dieu, with the happy result that relations between Magendie and Bernard were markedly improved.

Moreover, Magendie soon noticed the skill with which Bernard prepared anatomical specimens after autopsies in the ward. Still uncertain of the young man's name, he shouted from the end of the dissecting table, "See here, you, I'll take you as my *préparateur* at the College of France." Bernard's appointment in this capacity began in 1841, the second year of his internship. After the third or fourth lecture at which Bernard assisted, Magendie was so impressed by his skill that he remarked as he left the lecture room: "Well, you're a better man than I am!"

Bernard's duties at the laboratory included not only the preparation of experimental material for Magendie's demonstrations, but also such routine matters as procuring meat for the dogs kept in the cellars of the laboratory, hiring laboratory servants, and purchasing apparatus. Some correspondence over unpaid bills in 1843 indicates that Bernard was responsible for routine expenditure, but Magendie's signature was necessary before the bills were paid. Magendie was perpetually at war with the authorities about the amount of money budgeted to his course in experimental physiology, and Bernard later remarked that he had ample opportunity as Magendie's assistant "to observe the continual obstacles which the administration of the College put in his way."

Bernard was also very early made aware of the difficulties created for physiologists by well-meaning humanitarians. One of his favorite anecdotes was about a Quaker who visited Magendie at the laboratory, wearing the characteristic dress of his sect, a very wide-brimmed hat, a coat with upturned collar, and knee breeches. "I have heard thee spoken of," said the Quaker when he had made sure that he was addressing Magendie, "and I see I have not been misinformed; for I have been told thee does experiments on living animals. I have come to see thee to ask thee by what right thee does so, and to tell thee that thee must stop experiments of this kind because thee has no right to cause the death of animals or to make them suffer, and because thee sets a bad example and accustoms thy fellows to cruelty."

Bernard said that Magendie had ordered the experimental animal upon which they had been working to be taken away, and then had pointed out that experiments involving vivisection of animals aim at the benefit of humanity, that war is cruel but may be necessary, that hunting inflicts on animals more suffering than does physiology. The Quaker had replied that he was opposed to war and hunting also. Neither could convince the other, but Bernard observed that Magendie had treated the Quaker with the consideration due to his sincerity.

Meanwhile at the Hôtel-Dieu there were still occasions when all did not go smoothly. Magendie's opposition to bleeding in pneumonia cases was well known, although the practice was followed in all the other hospital services. Sometimes his interns felt duty-bound to bleed patients who were breathing with difficulty, in spite of the standing orders of the physician in charge. News of this finally got around to Magendie. When the question of bleeding pneumonia patients was brought up in the Academy of Sciences, Magendie boasted that such patients were not bled at the Hôtel-Dieu, and that they not only recovered, but their convalescence was more rapid. Another physician retorted: "It is true that you do not bleed your patients, but your interns bleed them behind your back." Bernard was at this time responsible for the ward Saint-Monique at the Hôtel-Dieu as well as for the laboratory, and it was upon him that Magendie descended with wrathful reproaches. After that, according to Bernard, pneumonia patients were not bled at the Hôtel-Dieu, although other patients were, on occasion, bled lightly to provide blood for experimental purposes.[1]

It was, indeed, convenient for Magendie to have an intern at the Hôtel-Dieu act also as his assistant at the College of France. He made use of both experimental and clinical material in his lectures, and specimens from hospital autopsies were often prepared for exhibition. Magendie was at this time investigating the composition and function of cerebrospinal fluid, a subject upon which

[1] Bernard was to carry on Magendie's crusade against bleeding to such effect that in his fifties he could jokingly complain that it hampered his researches. The Goncourts record that he amused the guests at a club dinner at the café Magny by remarking that bleeding had gone so out of fashion that he could no longer obtain blood for his demonstrations. He had been greatly obliged to an old-fashioned practitioner auditing his course who volunteered to bleed himself since he did it every day for the benefit of his flowers. Nevertheless, this medical superstition seems to have persisted in obscure corners in an astonishing way. George Orwell in his essay, "How the Poor Die," describes how he and other charity patients were bled in a Paris hospital in 1929. (George Orwell, *Shooting an Elephant and Other Essays,* 1950. Pp. 19-21.)

he published an important monograph in 1842. Bernard collected this fluid from cadavers at the Hôtel-Dieu, inventing a special technique for the purpose. He also made clinical studies of patients whose injuries resulted in loss of cerebrospinal fluid. In his preface to the 1842 monograph Magendie acknowledged that many of the new experiments were undertaken with the help of his *préparateur,* Bernard.

Bernard also assisted, in April, 1841, with some experiments designed to meet the criticisms of Longet, who had just published his attack on Magendie's work on "recurrent sensitivity." Magendie and Bernard were unsuccessful at this time in reproducing the phenomenon of sensitivity of the ventral roots, which had been observed during the lecture-demonstrations. They took great pains to examine the roots as soon as they were laid bare, in the hope of coming as close as possible to the natural physiological state. This detail is worth remembering, as it proved to be at the bottom of all their difficulties. They continued to repeat these experiments at intervals over a period of five years. Bernard, in particular, was dissatisfied with the inconsistency between what he had seen with his own eyes in 1839 and the results obtained in 1841. Magendie, as a strict empiricist, was content with the frank publication of his results both in 1839 and 1841. As we have seen in regard to his play, Bernard had the compulsion to finish what he had begun. It was actually he who in the end made the suggestion which was later to clear up the inconsistency.

All this work as Magendie's assistant must have left the young intern scant time for either his routine medical examinations or plans for his own scientific career. Nevertheless, he seems to have had the latter in view even while still an intern. He was not at all attracted by Magendie's empirical ideal of wandering about the realms of science picking up what he could find. He kept a notebook of physiological memoranda, which has been preserved, the first of a long series of notebooks associated with his scientific career. Part of it consists merely of abstracts of contemporary textbooks and memoirs, but it contains also original summaries of the known facts of the chief physiological processes, *e.g.*, respiration, circulation, nutrition, and secretion. Of greater interest are notations of what struck Bernard as being the blank spaces in contemporary knowledge of these subjects. For example, he raised the question whether the function of the liver does not include more than the secretion of bile. This is prophetic of his actual discovery of what that organ contributes to the process of nutrition. Other questions, especially in regard to animal heat and its control by the nervous system, are equally pertinent to the future course of his investigations. The notebook amounts to a rough sketch for a career and shows how early Bernard's ambition took a definite direction.

In May, 1843, Bernard set up that personal landmark which looms so large for a young scientist, his first published paper, "Anatomical and Physiological Researches on the Chorda Tympani, in Connection with Facial Paralysis." He was to return more than once to experimentation upon this little nerve, which takes its name from the fact that it crosses the inner surface of the eardrum (tympanum). Some of his fellow interns, discovering him at work on this project, made fun of him for writing such a long paper on so small a nerve.

The basis of the paper was Bernard's careful working out of the anatomy of the chorda tympani, in which he correctly established its origin in the seventh cranial nerve. After operating on a dog he happened to notice that the sense of taste was diminished on the side where the chorda tympani had been cut, and he attempted to define experimentally the function of the nerve. We can observe here the pattern (already noticed in Magendie's work) of readiness to follow up the implications of unforeseen phenomena occurring in the course of an experiment.

Bernard was not too fortunate in his first effort to make independent physiological deductions. He failed to see any interference with salivary secretion after the chorda tympani was cut, and concluded wrongly that this nerve has no influence on salivation. Nor did he arrive at a clean-cut conclusion about the part played by the chorda tympani in the sensation of taste. He was unable to satisfy himself that section of the nerve abolished taste completely. His inexperience appears in his failure to recognize that his method of testing for taste was faulty. It did not occur to him that the dry citric acid which he had placed on that side of the tongue for which the chorda tympani had been cut would dissolve in the mucus and spread to the side on which the nerve was uncut, to set off a delayed and feeble taste reaction.

He had been a little youthful and contemptuous at the beginning of his paper about earlier accounts of the chorda tympani, remarking that theory unsupported by experiment was apt to leave science with "only one more hypothesis." Even with the aid of experiment, he left science in the same plight, for he proposed that the chorda tympani he regarded as "not responsible for, but accessory to, taste." Moreover, fourteen years later he was still denying what we now know to be true, that the chorda tympani carries, in addition to motor fibers, sensory fibers for taste.

He was also engaged in 1843 in the initial studies for a comprehensive plan to trace "what becomes of the alimentary substances in nutrition." We have corroboration in his later writings that this was already a conscious design, and the admission that it was "much too vast." Thirty years later he was still working at what he had by that time realized was the mere beginning of the enterprise.

He began with sugar because he thought it was the substance easiest to identify and trace in the digestive system. His clinical experience in observing diabetic cases under Dr. Rayer should also be taken into account here. He injected cane-sugar solutions into the blood of animals and assured himself that this sugar, even when the amount was very small, reappeared in the urine. His next step, an original contribution, was to show that gastric juice acts upon cane sugar. He found that if sugar treated with gastric juice was injected into the blood, it could no longer be recovered in the urine. He had therefore shown that gastric juice modified cane sugar (in chemical terms, converted it into glucose) so as to make it assimilable in the blood.

Bernard used these results in the thesis for his degree of doctor of medicine, submitted in December, 1843, under the title *On Gastric Juice and the Part It Plays in Nutrition,* with a dedication to Magendie. His graduation in medicine was almost a casual event, for he had no intention of practicing as a physician if he could gain a foothold in the scientific hierarchy of Paris. His thesis was not merely the coping stone set to his career as a medical student, but the first stone brought to the building of his account of nutritive and metabolic processes in the human body.

4

THE FREE LANCE YEARS (1843–1845)

Twenty-five years ago, when I embarked on the career of experimental physiology . . . one needed to be upheld by a real passion for physiology and to have very great patience and courage in order not to be disheartened. Report on the Progress and Achievements of Physiology in France.

CLAUDE BERNARD WAS HALF WAY THROUGH HIS THIRTIETH year when he took his medical degree. For nine years he had been completely absorbed in his medical studies and his virtual apprenticeship to Magendie. The correspondence with Benoit Blanc ceased before his internship began and we have no other sidelight on that period. We do not know where Bernard lived in Paris (although we can guess that it was in the neighborhood of the working laboratory he set up in 1843 in the Commerce Saint-André-des-Arts, a number of houses there being regularly used as lodgings by medical students). He went home to Saint-Julien for the vintage in September and October, a custom never broken even in his busiest years. The only suggestion that he took any recreation in Paris is his recollection years afterwards of his visits to the art collections in the Louvre or to the theaters. That he knew the pictures in the Louvre extremely well appears from allusions in his letters. He remembered, for instance, the exact arrangement of the figures in a portrait of St. Thomas Aquinas by Benozzo Gozzoli, and used this to make a point about the relationship between the medieval nominalists and universalists. He recalled jingling rhymes which he had heard at the Palais-Royal while still a medical student and spoke of "my youth when I used to go to see performances of Scribe."

Having secured his degree, he was released from hospital work at the Hôtel-Dieu, but he stayed on as Magendie's research assistant at the College of France for another year. The story that Magendie grew jealous of his talented pupil and, in particular, objected to Bernard's use of his laboratory for personal researches must be related to the fact that for every year from 1844 to 1847 there is some record of collaboration between Magendie and Bernard. There was certainly no serious breach of relations between the two men. More probably a moment arrived when the subordinate post of *préparateur* no longer satisfied the dignity of even an impecunious Bernard. He had already held it longer than was usual when he resigned at the end of 1844. December of that year is the latest date at which his publications describe him as *préparateur* at the College of France.

His first attempt to secure an academic foothold independent of Magendie met with ignominious failure. In 1844 he took part in a competition for an assistant professorship in the section of anatomy and physiology of the Faculty of Medicine. The applicants were required to submit and defend a thesis. Bernard's was on the coloring matter of various bodily substances, blood, bile, urine, the eye, the skin, and the brain. He made a poor impression on the judges in the oral part of the competition by his awkward and hesitant delivery. Only one of the six judges, P. F. Blandin, voted for him. Blandin, professor of operative surgery since 1841, was a friend of Magendie and, moreover, had been chief demonstrator in anatomy when Bernard was a student in that subject. According to two of his French biographers, none of his contemporaries at that time predicted "anything more than the most modest of medical careers" for Bernard.

The collaboration between Magendie and Bernard in 1844 was a continuation of an inquiry into what they termed the "source of animal heat." They had been interested in this since 1842, when Gustav Magnus published his work in correction of Lavoisier's idea that the oxidation of respiration took place in the lungs. Bernard now carried out the spectacular experiment of inserting two long thermometers, one by way of the carotid artery and the other by way of the jugular vein, into the heart of a horse, in Bernard's words, "alive and on its feet." He found that the blood in the right ventricle was slightly warmer than that on the left, which indicated that blood on the way to the lungs had a higher temperature than blood leaving them, *i.e.,* combustion in the lungs could not be the source of body heat, as Lavoisier had supposed.

Bernard had horses at his disposal for experiments at this time because of Magendie's connection with a committee appointed at the request of the Minister of War to investigate equine hygiene and the treatment of horse glanders. Magendie and Bernard's friend Rayer were in disagreement as to whether this disease, marked in the horse by nasal ulcers and suppuration of the lungs, was communicable to man. On one occasion Bernard, Rayer, and Magendie were operating on a horse suffering from glanders and the animal tore the back of Bernard's hand, covering it with saliva. Rayer said, "Wash quickly."

Magendie, however, advised, "No, don't wash, you will hasten the absorption of the virus." After a moment's hesitation, Bernard said, "I'll wash, it's cleaner," and put his hand under the tap. Magendie's advice was sound so far as the physiological process of absorption was concerned, but Rayer's contention that man could be infected by horse glanders was finally proven to be right.

Magendie's interests were also represented in a paper published by Bernard in 1844, describing investigation of the action of two cranial nerves, the tenth and eleventh, on the vocal cords. Here as in his earliest paper, Bernard was betrayed into a false conclusion by a crudity in technique. The vocal cords are in fact controlled by the tenth cranial, but Bernard's method of pulling the eleventh out by the roots, thereby disturbing the neighboring roots of the tenth, led him to the erroneous conclusion that both nerves were involved.

The experiments had been undertaken to settle differences between Magendie and his persistent critic Longet, who raised fresh objections to the new results, although his own experiments were equally inconclusive. The real importance of this paper is the use to which Bernard put it. He submitted it for the prize in experimental physiology offered by the Academy of Sciences for 1845. This was a money prize, to help promising young scientists finance their researches. The whole affair proceeded in slow motion. It was December, 1846, before Bernard was invited to repeat his experiments before a committee of the Academy of Sciences. This was such an important occasion for him that he kept the official notice of it all his life. In April, 1847, three full years after the publication of the paper, the award to Bernard was announced. There is reason to assume that the award was finally made in recognition of what Bernard had accomplished while he was waiting for it.

In the meantime Bernard's most pressing problem was to find a place to carry on his independent work in the chemistry of nutrition, the first steps of which he had published in his doctoral thesis. The friend who provided him with working space outside of Magendie's laboratory was Théophile Jules Pelouze. Like Bernard he had been a pharmacist's apprentice and had also served an internship under Magendie. Coming under the influence of Gay-Lussac, he later studied in Germany with Liebig, and was now established as a chemist.

In the early summer of 1844, Pelouze passed on to Bernard a gift he had received of the arrows tipped with the South American poison curare which are used by Indian natives in hunting and in battle. Bernard at once tried the poison on a frog and observed its characteristic effect, immobility followed by death. But he did not then carry the experiment beyond a careful autopsy. He was to return to a complete investigation of curare a few years later.

What really occupied him in Pelouze's laboratory can be gathered from a story which he afterwards told of an early clash with the law over using animals for physiological experiments:

> I was doing experiments on digestion with the help of the stomach fistula which Blondlot had devised, in a laboratory which my friend Pelouze had in the rue Dauphine. One day a celebrated Berlin surgeon, Dieffenbach, came to Paris. Pelouze, who knew him, mentioned my experiments; he wanted to see them, and one day, after lunching together, we went to the laboratory in the rue Dauphine and I inserted a silver cannula in a dog's stomach while Dieffenbach looked on. The animal was let loose as usual to recover from this not very serious operation.

The next day, when we returned, the dog had disappeared. Although the yard gate was shut, the dog had escaped by a vent-hole of a neighbor's cellar and had thus reached the street. . . . I regretted only the loss of my instrument which the dog had taken with it.

I thought no more of the matter until two or three days later I was visited early in the morning by a man who said that the police commissioner of the district wished to speak to me. . . . I went the same day to see the commissioner and clear up the mystery about what he wanted of me. When I gave my name the elderly commissioner in a very chilly manner asked me to follow him. He took me into the next room, where I found his wife and daughter lavishing attention and caresses on a small dog which I at once recognized as the one I had operated on two days before for Dieffenbach and Pelouze. "Do you know this poor animal?" the commissioner asked solemnly, indicating his dog. "Certainly," I replied, "and I also recognize my silver cannula, which I am very pleased to recover." The dog recognized me too and greeted me in a friendly way. Then the commissioner launched upon a stern lecture in which he said I had placed myself in a serious situation by taking his dog, and his wife and daughter burst into grief-stricken reproaches over my cruelty. I hastened to cut short this scene with a firm denial of the accusations made against me. . . . I first assured the commissioner that I did not pick up dogs, that the animals which I used in my experiments were supplied to me by people whom the police employed to collect stray dogs. I reminded him (for it was July) that the walls of the quarter were covered with posters to the effect that no dog was to be allowed out unless muzzled or on a leash, and that his dog had probably not been so equipped when it was taken. . . . I reassured the commissioner and his wife and daughter about the dog, took out my cannula, and promised to come back the next day to see if the animal needed any attention.

> I kept my word and visited them several times; at the end of a week or ten days, the wound was completely healed and no trace of the operation remained. From that time on I enjoyed the protection of the commissioner and the approval of his wife and daughter. More than once the commissioner was of use to me in getting at the truth of the complaints which were frequently made against me and I stayed on in the quarter behind the Medical School because I knew that no hostile move would be made against me without warning.[1]

The actual building is gone but the site of the private laboratory to which Bernard here refers can still be found in the passage entered by archways either from the Boulevard Saint-Germain or the rue Saint-André-des-Arts. The passage still has the name which it had in Bernard's time, Commerce Saint-André-des-Arts, and is still frequented by those in search of modest shelter for their pursuits. Bernard liked to recall this little backwater in the Latin Quarter, still harboring relics of the history of medieval and revolutionary Paris, as the scene of his early independent work. Here, he said, he had often dreamed over his experiments and suddenly come upon the solution of difficulties that had long baffled him. Visited a hundred years later on a sunny day the spot, secluded from the modern roar of the nearby boulevard, has a quiet gaiety, accented by a few bright geraniums in window boxes.

Bernard's studies in digestion mentioned in the police commissioner anecdote were concerned with the properties of gastric juice and were carried out in collaboration with another friend, a talented young chemist, Charles Barreswill. On the ground of his experiments with Barres-

[1] This story is usually taken from the *Report* of 1867, but is here quoted from the more conversational account given in the manuscript notes posthumously published in 1947 under the title *Principles of Experimental Medicine.*

will, Bernard rejected the analysis of two American chemists, Dunglison and Silliman, which reported the presence of free hydrochloric acid in gastric juice. Dunglison and Silliman worked with samples of gastric juice provided by their fellow countryman, the brilliant physician-physiologist, William Beaumont, who had obtained them through the permanent fistula left by an abdominal gunshot wound suffered by his patient, Alexis Saint-Martin.

Bernard and Barreswill held that the free acid in gastric juice was not hydrochloric but lactic acid. Their results have been explained as arising from the continued presence of food in the stomachs of fasting animals from which gastric juice was collected by means of a cannula like the one Bernard mentioned in his anecdote. Bernard qualified his finding by saying that he did not think that lactic acid was specifically indispensable to digestion in the stomach; an acid reaction was all that was necessary. He demonstrated that the real digestive agent in gastric juice was the organic matter whose digestive qualities were destroyed by heating to 85° or 90° Centigrade. Since destruction by heat is a distinctive characteristic of enzymes, Bernard's position may be quite well expressed in the familiar modern terms that digestion in the stomach is performed by the enzyme pepsin (the name given to it by Schwann in 1846), which acts as an organic catalyst in an acid medium. But Bernard was wrong in denying that the free acid in gastric juice was hydrochloric acid.

In his subsequent collaboration with Barreswill, which amounted to a paper a year from 1844 to 1849, Bernard was to find the young chemist's recent discovery of a copper tartrate reagent very valuable as a test for sugar. This test was new in 1844, although today schoolboys use it in a slightly modified form and are familiar with the striking change in color of Fehling's solution, which, when heated with sugar turns from blue to green, then to yellow, and finally to red.

The association of Bernard and Barreswill had its amusing side. Although the two young men had chemistry in common, they did not see eye to eye as to how life should be conducted outside the laboratory. Troubled by Barreswill's habit of drinking cognac after every meal as an aid to digestion, Bernard offered to demonstrate, experimentally, that cognac did not have this effect. He presently reported that he had fed a dog different kinds of food and in each case topped off the meal with cognac. Barreswill wished Bernard would do the same for him. Bernard then reported that on opening the dog's stomach a few hours after the meal, he observed that digestion had been arrested and some of the food had not been acted upon in the normal way by the gastric juice at all. He then asked Barreswill to draw his own conclusions. Barreswill solemnly gave his conclusion that cognac was not meant for dogs. He collaborated, however, in further experiments demonstrating that in moderate doses alcohol excited gastric secretion and in larger doses arrested it.

In 1845 Bernard embarked on several enterprises either to increase his income or to make up for earnings relinquished when he resigned as Magendie's paid assistant. He prepared anatomical dissections to be drawn by the lithographer H. Jacob for Marc Jean Bourgery's well-known anatomical atlas.[2] He also collaborated with Charles Huette on an illustrated textbook of surgery frequently reprinted between 1846 and 1854. The book was

---

[2] *Traité complet de l'anatomie de l'homme* (Complete Atlas of Human Anatomy) by M. J. Bourgery and H. Jacob. The first edition appeared in a series of volumes from 1832 to 1854 without mention of Bernard as a contributor. In a second edition his name was used, although he had made no new contribution, and his connection with the first edition had been very brief.

translated into five European languages and copies were given to the surgeons of the United States Army during the Civil War.

Less successful was Bernard's attempt to set up a teaching laboratory in partnership with Lasègue, his old friend and fellow-teacher at the girls' school. This venture was housed in a sort of shed in the rue Saint-Jacques, near the Pantheon, then a region of somber alleys; but the fees collected from their five or six pupils did not even cover the cost of the rent and the rabbits for the experiments. At about the same time Bernard was obliged to give up his quarters in the Commerce Saint-André-des-Arts, the friendly police commissioner being no longer able to stem the anti-vivisectionist tide of rumor. Certain women of the quarter insisted that children as well as animals were brought to the laboratory in sacks.

In the summer of 1845, while his affairs were still in a precarious state, Bernard married Marie Françoise Martin, daughter of a Paris physician. The marriage was arranged in a typically French manner through Pelouze, a friend of the Martins as well as of Bernard. Pelouze conceived the idea with the object of keeping Bernard in Paris at a time when he was so depressed that he contemplated, as he had while still a medical student, a return to Saint-Julien and practice as a country doctor.

Marie Françoise Bernard was twenty-six at the time of her marriage, six years younger than her husband. She brought a dowry which looked rather impressive beside the meager possessions of her husband set forth in the marriage contract. Bernard took his bride home to 5 rue Pont-de-Lodi, which was near his laboratory. The furnishings of the apartment, his library, his clothes, and his cash-on-hand, carefully listed in the contract, had a total value of 9,800 francs. The bride brought an official dowry of 60,000 francs, two-thirds of which was paid in cash, the remaining third, paid in yearly instalments, with interest added, provided an income of 5000 francs a year over a period of nine years. She also brought her trousseau, personal savings of 2,000 francs, and an inheritance of 3,000 francs from her godmother. Even these last-named sums were entrusted to the groom along with everything else, according to the custom of the day. Magendie backed Bernard in this personal venture, his name and Mme. Magendie's appearing along with those of Pelouze and the toxicologist Orfila (another scientist friend) on the marriage contract. The bride's brother signed for her, which suggests that she was orphaned. There is no mention of any member of Bernard's family from Saint-Julien.

5

THE FIRST MAJOR DISCOVERY (1846–1849)

Chance observation of this fact put me on the alert, awakening in my mind the thought that pancreatic juice might well cause the emulsion of fatty materials and consequently their absorption by the lymphatic vessels. Introduction to the Study of Experimental Medicine.

THE BEGINNING OF BERNARD'S REALLY EFFECTIVE AND ORIGinal scientific work, culminating in his first important discovery, followed closely on his marriage. During the two years after he took his medical degree, he made himself useful to Magendie in miscellaneous researches and acquired some valuable connections with chemists and a great deal of even more valuable experience in chemical and operative techniques. But his scientific achievements can very nearly be reduced to a catalogue of his errors. Moreover, he had failed to secure an academic post and was again unsuccessful in 1845 when he applied for a seat left vacant in the Academy of Medicine.

In the early months of 1846 things began to happen. We may guess that certain tensions had been released, or that the immediate economic security provided by his wife's dowry relieved him temporarily from distracting anxieties, or even that his new responsibilities provided a spur to a temperament tending to dreamy reflection and indolence. Bernard recognized this quality in himself. He once wrote, explaining why he had not "begun to work," "This indolence of mind is quite habitual with me; when nothing is pressing me, my thoughts turn readily into a revery feeding on my memories."

We must not imagine that Bernard's investigation of the function of the pancreas was deliberately undertaken, that he surveyed the subject and drew up a plan of research. The events leading to his discovery had more connection with the routine of Magendie's laboratory than with his own work of the moment with Barreswill on injecting starch and sugar into the blood. Magendie had turned over the facilities at the College of France to studies of digestive fluids. Bernard revived Magendie's procedure of twenty-five years earlier for the collection of pancreatic juice and repeated Magendie's demonstration that this fluid was coagulated by heat. Bernard had also cleared up a discrepancy between the work of Magendie and Brodie by pointing out that the anatomical arrangement of the bile duct in cats differs from that in dogs. We shall see that it was fortunate for him that he had just at this time been put on the alert for differences in the anatomy of various animals in the location of ducts of secretory organs.

Even when he embarked deliberately on an investigation it was not Bernard's habit to begin with the literature of the subject. We have his own word for this in a letter of 1869:

> Allow me to explain briefly my habitual way of working. I never form an opinion from those of other people. On the contrary, I always try to work out first my own

> conception of the matter and it is only after that that I read what has been written on the subject.

He advised his pupils to proceed in the same way and not to worry if their observations only corroborated those of others, since they were at least learning to *see* for themselves.

We may therefore assume that Bernard began his work on the pancreas equipped only with the general information which anyone in his field would have. He knew that Malpighi in the seventeenth century had observed that the pancreas had a duct, a discovery which had undermined the view that the organ was merely a cushion for the stomach to rest upon. He knew how Regnier de Graaf, in an operation described in 1664, had obtained pancreatic juice by inserting a duck's quill in the pancreatic duct, and that de Graaf had declared pancreatic juice to be one of the fundamental digestive secretions, but had drawn the wrong conclusion from merely tasting it that it was acid. About 1820 Magendie had devised an improved technique for the collection of pure pancreatic juice. In 1844 another French investigator, Gabriel Valentin, had observed that juice expressed from the pancreas had a digestive effect upon starch.

On a winter morning early in 1846, some rabbits intended for use in experiments with Barreswill were brought to Bernard's laboratory. When they urinated, Bernard observed that the urine was clear and acid. Ordinarily, the urine of rabbits, which are herbivores, is turbid and alkaline. Since clearness and acidity are characteristics of the urine of carnivores, it occurred to Bernard that these rabbits on their way to market had not been fed for a long time and that they had been transformed by their fasting into carnivorous animals, living on their own tissues. This, of course, was merely a guess at the truth, although a very shrewd one. Bernard immediately tested it experimentally by giving the rabbits grass to eat; the next sample of their urine proved to be turbid and alkaline. The rabbits were made to fast for 24 to 36 hours and then fed, and it was found that after fasting their urine was always clear and acid and after a feeding of grass it became turbid and alkaline. Bernard then made the rabbits literally carnivores by feeding them cold boiled beef, which they would eat if they were hungry. As long as this diet was continued, their urine remained clear and acid. This result he published in March, 1846.

Magendie's interest was aroused and he reversed Bernard's experiment by feeding a dog on potatoes and lard. He found that the dog now had the cloudy and alkaline urine of a herbivore and noted also that its blood contained sugar derived from a starchy diet. Bernard had the idea of turning himself into a herbivore, and after subsisting on potatoes, cauliflower, carrots, green peas, salad, and fruit for twenty-four hours, he found that his urine was alkaline. When he breakfasted on bread and coffee with milk, and dined on soup, pigeon, green peas, cheese, and coffee, it was acid.

Following his customary experimental routine, Bernard killed and autopsied the meat-fed rabbits, being especially interested to see if meat was digested in the same way in rabbits as in carnivorous animals. He found all the phenomena of an excellent digestion and also made what turned out to be the crucial observation for his discovery. He saw "a very abundant white, milky chyle"[1]

[1] *Chyle* is a term for food acted upon by bile from the liver and pancreatic juice, as *chyme* is the term for food mingled only with saliva and the gastric juice of the stomach. The *duodenum* is the portion of the small intestine immediately below the stomach, and the *pylorus* is the opening from the stomach into the duodenum, which is guarded by a strong sphincter muscle.

in the lymphatic vessels, or lacteals, into which the products of intestinal digestion are absorbed, to be conveyed eventually into the blood stream. He noticed that the distended lacteals "were first visible coming away from the small intestine at the lower part of the duodenum about thirty centimeters below the pylorus." He was immediately curious to discover what caused this difference. Perhaps some recollection of the difference he had observed the year before in the anatomical arrangement of the pancreatic ducts in dogs and cats stirred in his mind. He suddenly saw that the insertion of the rabbit's principal pancreatic duct was very low in the intestine as compared with the dog, and "near the exact place where the lacteals began to contain chyle made white and milky *by emulsion of fatty nutritive materials.*" He described the conclusion he drew from this coincidence as follows:

> Instinctively I made this syllogism: the white chyle is due to emulsion of the fat; now in rabbits white chyle is formed at the level where pancreatic juice is poured into the intestine; therefore it is pancreatic juice that makes the emulsion of fat and forms the white chyle.

Bernard always felt that the moment of this observation was one of the high points of his life as an experimenter. He described it more than once in his later years, notably in his *Introduction to the Study of Experimental Medicine.* He regarded the sequence of events which began with the starved rabbits on his laboratory table as a first-class instance of the experimental method in action. He remarked that Bacon had compared scientific investigation to the sport of hunting, with observed phenomena as the game, which sometimes presents itself when we are looking for it, and sometimes when we are not, or are looking for another sort of game. On this occasion he had brought down game he had not been looking for. He had acquired the habit in Magendie's laboratory of being continually on the watch for unexpected developments in experiments on living material. There was even an element of luck in the situation, if we can accept the evidence of German physiologists who attempted to repeat Bernard's experiment and found that the disposition of the fat and the lacteal contents which he observed in the rabbit was not invariable but occurred only when the abdomen was opened at a particular time after the fat had been taken.

What was not given to Bernard by luck or by training was the imaginative swiftness with which he grasped the implications of what he saw, and the ingenuity and patience with which he at once entered the test-tube phase of the investigation. He devised a whole series of experiments to test his theory that neutral fats are rendered absorbable through the action of the pancreas and its secretion. The idea was entirely new, for up to this time the most positive view of the function of the pancreas had been based on Valentin's observation that pancreatic juice had an effect on starch similar to that shown by saliva, and the pancreas had in fact sometimes been described as the abdominal salivary gland. Bernard worked at his experiments for more than two years before he published his results in a preliminary form in April, 1848. More work that year enabled him to bring out a more extended account in February, 1849. It was completeness which he sought, not secrecy for the detail of his work. During the first two years of his researches he had occasion to repeat his experiments before many French and foreign scientists. His final word on the part played in digestion by pancreatic juice did not, however, come until he published his *Memoir on the Pancreas* in 1856.

When Bernard was at last ready to lay asi
the pancreas, he had established as the specia
pancreatic juice in regard to fat that it has the
tion of saponifying it, *i.e.,* breaking it down int
and glycerine. He demonstrated this not only f
atic juice collected through a fistula, but for crus
creatic tissue, mixed with fat and kept at body t
ture for a short time.

While the more original part of his work was conc
with the effect of the pancreatic secretion in the dige
of fats, Bernard did not neglect its role in the digestio
the other two principal alimentary substances, starches a
proteins. He corroborated the work of Valentin, demo
strating that pancreatic juice is the digestive fluid most ac
tive in transforming starch into sugar.

His account of the digestion of proteins was much less complete. He held rightly that the digestion of proteins was perfected by the pancreatic juice but believed wrongly that its action was directly dependent upon the prior action of the bile. (He had been the first, in 1844, in studies on dogs, to call attention to certain conspicuous features attending the digestive action of bile on proteins.) Perhaps his chief service to the study of the pancreatic digestion of proteins was the impetus he gave his German pupil, Willy Kühne, who was to become professor of physiology at Amsterdam and Heidelberg.

Kühne isolated the protein-splitting enzyme trypsin, a constituent of pancreatic juice, in 1876, and formulated the doctrine of enzymes, which brought the study of the digestion of proteins into a new phase. The problem was handed on from one investigator to another. The activation of trypsin in the duodenum by enterokinase (a substance present in the intestinal juice) was discovered in the laboratory of the Russian physiologist Ivan Petrovich Pavlov two scientific generations after Bernard. Great ad-

vances in the science of biochemistry had to be made before a real explanation of the action of pancreatic juice on proteins could properly be attempted. Bernard was not himself a trained chemist, even for his day, although he was fully aware of the dependence of physiological investigation upon chemistry. The observations which had carried him so far on the way to the elucidation of the function of the pancreas had been those of a physiologist.

As a physiologist, Bernard naturally sought to discover the effect upon the digestive process of depriving the animal of its pancreas. His many attempts to depancreatize dogs by surgical means failed and the operation was first performed successfully by Joseph von Mering and Oscar Minkowski in 1889. It became a commonplace of laboratory procedure during the 1920's while the effects of insulin in combating diabetes were being worked out. The procedure which Bernard found most effective for putting the pancreas out of action was to inject into its ducts melted fats which would solidify at body temperature. Many of the animals died of peritonitis, but some survived long enough to establish that suppressing the flow of pancreatic juice into the intestine prevented normal digestion of such foods as fat pork chops and potatoes. Not only fat and starch, but traces of meat were found unaltered in the feces.

Almost everyone today associates dysfunction of the pancreas with the disease of diabetes. That the pancreas can suffer another dysfunction, an inability to digest fats, starches, and proteins, is not so generally understood. Bernard's contribution relates to the latter. However, in a subsequent experiment, he seems to have come within an ace of identifying the blood sugar controlling function of the pancreas—and missed it.

On October 3, 1849, Bernard operated on a poodle,

young and quite sturdy, to produce a pancreatic fistula. Something went wrong, and the secretion obtained had no emulsifying action on fat. The dog ate voraciously, but grew thin and weak. Bernard exhibited it to some of his colleagues and took it home with him the third week after the operation. He noticed that it seemed exhausted by the effort of following him up and down stairs. In the sixth week the dog died in a state of great emaciation although it had continued to eat. The autopsy disclosed almost total disappearance of the pancreas, the remaining bit being quite black. Bernard commented that the experiment had been the equivalent of removal of the pancreas, and noted the symptoms as "severe emaciation accompanied by voracious appetite," and the outcome as "death by wasting away." He was apparently prevented from making the diagnosis of diabetes, so strongly suggested by these symptoms, because he failed to find sugar in the urine. It is just possible that his test for sugar may not have been sensitive enough to detect the amount which would have been present in the urine on the diet of sheep's head which the dog seemed to favor.

In any case, the emaciation and wasting away in spite of voracious appetite is best accounted for as being due to a failure of the pancreatic function distinct from the one upon which Bernard's attention was focused. The work of von Mering and Minkowski finally led to the recognition that in addition to secreting a digestive juice into the intestine, the pancreas also furnished an essential substance now identified by the researches of Banting, Best, Collip, and Macleod as insulin, whose deficiency produced diabetic symptoms. Bernard failed to draw the conclusion to which his association of diabetic symptoms with destruction of the pancreas in his experimental animal pointed. The notion of a double function of the pancreas did not occur to him, as that of a double function of the liver was so soon to do. Still, the precision of his observations pointed the way to the discovery which, because of its more spectacular medical results, will be regarded by many as greater than his own. Moreover, his work on the liver, as we shall see, was to contribute the *idea* (of an internal secretion) which was fundamental in solving the problem of the relation of the pancreas to diabetes.

The value of Bernard's work on the pancreas was immediately acknowledged in Paris. The 1849 memoir was submitted for the Academy of Sciences prize in experimental physiology, and won him the award for the second time in 1850. At the beginning of 1847 Bernard had been elected to the Philomathic Society, of which most of the distinguished scientists of Paris were members, many of whom, like Magendie, the chemist Berthelot, and the younger physiologists Milne Edwards, Brown-Séquard, and Longet, were already well known to him. He was also one of a group of younger French scientists who in May, 1848, founded the Society of Biology, which they hoped would be more liberal and hospitable to unestablished reputations than the Academies. Bernard's old friend, Dr. Rayer, was elected president, and he himself was chosen one of the two vice-presidents. He was very active from the beginning, and the reports of the weekly meetings are almost a running commentary on the progress of his research.

Magendie expressed his enthusiasm for Bernard's accomplishment by urging his nomination as Chevalier of the Légion d'Honneur, and the red ribbon was conferred in April, 1849. The announcement was to be a surprise. When the copy of the *Moniteur* containing it was shown to him, Bernard immediately exclaimed that it must be to Magendie that he owed the unexpected decoration. He was also annoyed to find a misprint which credited him with "excellent work on the musical (apparently instead of "medical") properties of the pancreas."

There is a photograph of Bernard with the Légion ribbon conspicuous in a button-hole, dated 1849. It shows a rather striking-looking young man (he was now 36), the broad, high forehead made more massive by the beginning of a recession at the temples. The hair, worn rather long, extends into muttonchop whiskers at the back of the jaw. The lips and chin are firm and clean-shaven. The fine bony structure of the head is much clearer than in later photographs, which show a slight puffiness of the flesh. The eyes are direct, dark, a little veiled by the eyelids. The impression is of a man with great reserves of strength, pride, and self-reliance.

The most important reward which Bernard's successes brought was his return in 1847 to the College of France, this time as *suppléant,* or substitute lecturer, to Magendie, who, having already retired from active duty at the Hôtel-Dieu, now relinquished his summer course of lectures to Bernard, while continuing for another five years to give the winter course himself. Bernard opened his first lecture rather forbiddingly by announcing: "The scientific medicine which it is my duty to teach you does not exist." Later, recalling the challenging introduction of his first course, he explained that he believed that medicine might become a true science as soon as physiology was sufficiently developed to provide it with a basis. His lecture demonstrations were carried out according to the traditions which Magendie had established since he could already rely upon his own researches for his material.

At the time Bernard was beginning his work on the pancreas, he turned aside for a final attack on the problem of "recurrent sensitivity," which went back to the period of his first association with Magendie in 1839 and 1841. He had returned to the problem briefly in 1844, but in January and February of 1846, and again at the end of May and June (apparently after the first excitement over the pancreas had subsided), he performed a series of experiments which established that if the animals were allowed time to recover from the shock of operation, the phenomenon of recurrent sensitivity appeared consistently. The matter was dropped again until early in 1847, when Magendie's work on the spinal nerve roots was again under attack in the Academy of Sciences. Both Magendie and Bernard published papers finally silencing those who had baited Magendie with charges of experimental inconsistency. Since Magendie freely acknowledged the help he had received from Bernard in meeting this attack, it was almost as if Bernard had vindicated the honor of the Chair of Medicine at the College of France as a preliminary to being asked to share its functions.

6

THE LIVER AS A SOURCE OF SUGAR (1848–1850)

The prevailing theory at this time, which was naturally my proper starting point, assumed that the sugar present in animals comes exclusively from foods, and that it is destroyed in the animal organism by phenomena of combustion, i.e., of respiration. Introduction to the Study of Experimental Medicine.

IT HAD TAKEN ONLY A LITTLE MORE THAN FIVE YEARS TO transform Bernard from an obscure, newly fledged medical graduate, of whom no one (except possibly Magendie) had any great hopes, into a young scientist who spoke with the authority of his first major success. The semiretirement of Magendie had made Bernard heir apparent to the Chair of Medicine at the College of France, and he was not under the necessity of maintaining a private working place after 1847. His routine led him from his apartment to the College and back again, sometimes with one of his experimental animals at his heels. From the beginning of 1849, he unfailingly put in an appearance, on Saturday afternoons at three o'clock, at the Society of Biology, which met in the amphitheater of his fellow vice-president, Charles Robin, in the *École pratique*. There he contributed rather more than his share to the exchange of scientific information, curiosities, and anomalies, which were the delight of its members. Only the irrepressible Brown-Séquard contrived to take up more space in the minutes than Bernard. This circumscribed existence seems to have completely absorbed him, although its returns, from the economic point of view, were meager. Since he did not practice medicine, that was to be expected.

Real misfortune had touched him when his first child, a son, Louis Henri, born in May, 1846, died at the age of three months. A year later, on August 20, 1847, a daughter, Jeanne Henriette, was born. Jeanne had been the name of Bernard's mother, but the child was always called "Tony," this name being used eventually even on official documents. On May 9, 1847, Bernard's father died at Saint-Julien at the age of sixty-two. His legacy to his son consisted chiefly of his debts, which Bernard assumed without protest, setting aside a considerable sum every year to meet this obligation until it was discharged.

The meagerness of the surviving detail of Bernard's private life for these years of his main achievements suggests that they were completely filled with his work. Later, when he was less absorbed, he wrote the letters, cultivated the friendships, and published the reflections which exhibit other facets of his life. All his reminiscences of the time from 1846 to 1859 relate to his scientific activities. He used an odd simile once to express his capacity for work in his prime. He said he had been like "an iron bar painted to represent a reed." If his pace had been a little indolent before his first success, after it his stride was relentless; but we must not forget that the ground he covered was a field filled with a network of unexplored paths, where there is now a broad highway.

Bernard regarded his work on the liver as an example of how research, starting from a generally accepted hypothesis, may sometimes overthrow that hypothesis. In this case a theory of Lavoisier's had recently been revived in the famous essay published in Paris in 1841 by the chemists Dumas and Boussingault. The theory held that animals were incapable of building up compounds supplied them in food from plants. The German chemist Liebig had challenged this view, claiming that fat could be made by herbivorous animals out of starches and sugars; but in France the tendency was to support Dumas. The matter was put to the test of numerous experiments, and by 1845 Dumas had been almost driven to admit that all the sugar in the milk of a bitch could not be accounted for as having been derived from the meat on which she had been fed, but with the qualification that she had chewed her hay bedding and might have got sugar from that source. Bernard was inclined to be impatient with experiments of the kind upon which the chemists were relying, since they merely compared what went into the animal with what came out. This, he said, was like trying to tell what happens inside a house by watching what goes in by the door and comes out by the chimney. His own aim was "to follow step by step and experimentally all the transformations of substances which the chemists were explaining theoretically."

Another accepted doctrine was that sugar in the blood was a phenomenon characteristic of diabetes and not a normal occurrence in healthy animals. Magendie's experiments were the first to cast doubt upon this view, but Bernard planned a more elaborate series, in which animals were fed on both starchy and meat diets and even kept for some days without food. In all cases, both where the stomach and intestine contained sugar and where they were free of sugar, the test for sugar in the blood was positive, while in the urine it was negative. The blood tested was taken from the cavities of the heart. Bernard concluded that the presence of sugar as a normal constituent of the blood of healthy animals was beyond doubt and that the doctrine that animals could derive a particular substance, like sugar, only directly from their diet was seriously called in question.

The disproof of two theories was, to Bernard, merely a by-product and a fresh starting point. For him a theory in science had a strictly temporary jurisdiction; it was useful as a summing up of known facts about a particular subject at a particular time. If contradictory facts were brought to light, these must be accepted and the theory abandoned. If possible, it must be replaced by a new theory covering the new facts. Even a discarded theory was not to be despised if it had stimulated investigation which unearthed new facts.

After what he himself called "some fumbling," he decided that the most likely source of sugar in the blood of animals would be one of the glandular organs of the abdomen. He killed animals, some fasting, the others in full digestion of a starch- and sugar-free diet, and opening the abdomen immediately drew blood from the portal vein near its entrance to the liver. This blood contained even more sugar than the sample from the right ventricle of the heart. Since there was no sugar in the contents of the intestine away from which the blood in the portal vein was flowing, Bernard decided that the blood rich in sugar had seeped back into the portal vein from the liver when pressure on the vein was removed by the opening of the abdomen. He now tested an extract of the tissues of the liver, which proved to be rich in sugar. At this point, in August, 1848, he sent a communication to the Academy of Sciences indicating that he had obtained positive evidence of the presence of sugar in the liver of a dog fed on meat exclusively.

In the following year he elaborated the experiment of collecting blood from the portal vein by tying off veins from the intestine, spleen, and pancreas and ligaturing the portal vein closer to its entrance to the liver. In this way he satisfied himself that the liver was either the source or storage point of sugar in the organism.

His own belief (he did not feel that he had accomplished a proof) was that the liver *secreted* sugar, and he now cast about for experimental means of interfering with or controlling the hypothetical secretion. He recalled that Magendie had produced a flow of tears by stimulating the appropriate nerve, and had stopped the flow by cutting the same nerve. Perhaps the secretion of sugar was controlled through a nerve in the same way as the secretion of tears. He tried cutting the vagi (or tenth pair of cranial nerves), but the operation consistently resulted in death. The autopsies revealed what he expected—absence of sugar in the blood and liver. But he got no results when he tried to increase the production of sugar by stimulating the vagi. This is an example of the proof and counterproof sought for in Bernard's method. It must always be shown that a given condition precedes or accompanies a phenomenon and *also* that the phenomenon disappears when the condition is removed before we can assume that the given condition is the immediate cause of the phenomenon. This procedure Bernard considered an "essential characteristic of experimental reasoning."

In the present case, he reflected that his method of stimulation might have been at fault and remembered that he had been able to induce secretion in the salivary glands by wounding the controlling nerve at its origin in the brain. He therefore laid bare the floor of the fourth ventricle of the brain and punctured the spot from which the vagi issued. He succeeded the very first time in "rendering the animal diabetic," to use his own expression, *i.e.*, in increasing the concentration of sugar in its blood. In an hour the blood and urine of the rabbit used were charged with sugar. In his work on blood sugar Bernard, although concentrating on the physiological problem of organic function, obviously anticipated that his findings might eventually have some bearing on the clinical problem of the origin of diabetic symptoms. But he was not on the path which led to the solution of the clinical problem. The territory in which he was pioneering was too unexplored for a direct approach.

In April, 1849, at one of the Saturday sessions of the Society of Biology Bernard announced his actual finding, that wounding the floor of the fourth ventricle, both in rabbits and dogs, caused the appearance of sugar in the blood and urine. This was his regular way of putting what he thought was a significant observation on the record even before he had fully explored its implications. He was not at the end of his difficulties, for he was unable for a time to repeat his first experiment. He persisted until he found that the area for a successful puncture was a very small one, which he had by sheer luck hit upon in the first animal used. He then tried to give a counterproof by cutting the vagi before he made the puncture, and found to his dismay that sugar appeared as abundantly as when they were intact. His hypothesis about the influence of the vagi on secretion in the liver had to be abandoned, but he was sure that there was nervous control by some other pathway.

He eventually decided that both the vagi and the sympathetic nerves were involved in a reflex arc, since he could cancel the effect of the brain puncture by cutting the spinal cord just above the exit of the splanchnic nerves, which belong to the sympathetic system. The relation of the sympathetic system to the adrenals was not yet known, and Bernard was wrong in supposing that the sympathetics acted directly on the liver. However, the production of "artificial diabetes" by piqûre, or puncture, became a famous operative demonstration, always associated with Bernard's name, and frequently repeated in physiological laboratories to show the control exercised by the nervous system over production of sugar. It is not without clinical importance, since in intracranial hemorrhages the resulting pressure may produce the typical rise in blood sugar.

Bernard summed up his results in "The Origin of Sugar in the Animal Economy," presented to the Society of Biology in August, 1849, and "On a New Function of the Liver" presented to the Academy of Sciences in October, 1850. In the latter he announced an improvement in the technique for obtaining blood which had passed through the liver—tying off the portal vein close to the liver and comparing blood drawn from below this ligature, *i.e.,* blood before it entered the liver, with blood from the hepatic veins, *i.e.,* blood that had traversed the liver. He found no sugar in the portal vein below the ligature and abundant sugar in the hepatic veins. For this work the Academy of Sciences in 1851 awarded to Bernard its prize in experimental physiology for the third time.

He presented virtually the same material, with the addition of a chapter on analogous investigations in invertebrate animals, in the thesis which he defended March 17, 1853, to obtain the degree of Doctor of Natural Sciences. We find here a very neat demonstration taken from the behavior of the common snail to illustrate the double secretive function of the liver. In the snail the gland which corresponds to the vertebrate liver has two different secretions; it secretes sugar while digestion is going on, and bile during abstinence from food. Bile, therefore, accumulates in the stomach in the intervals between eating, and at the next meal as the food descends the digestive tract, it meets this store of bile, and digestion and the secretion of sugar begin. In man the bile is stored between periods of digestive activity in the gall bladder, a mere elaboration of the same process.

We may judge of Bernard's increasing importance in scientific Paris by reports sent back to America in 1850 and 1851 by young American physicians completing their medical studies in European hospitals and laboratories. They attended his lecture demonstrations and perhaps visited the laboratory, where Bernard received strangers with "unvarying affability" and "patient and kind attention."

Bernard never headed a research school. His laboratory was inadequate to accommodate even the few pupils he had. The contrast here with his German contemporary, Karl Ludwig, is marked. In his *Introduction* Bernard speaks of the solitary scientist "who discovers and explores a whole scientific question unaided" (which for the most part describes his own case), and contrasts this way of working with that of a group of specialists coordinating their gifts as observers, organizers, or systematizers. He had no feeling against specialization, provided it was not assumed that any one man had the right to "make generalization his specialty," while relying on other workers to gather observations. He thought every scientist should maintain contact with the realities upon which his science is based. It should be added that Ludwig did this. He worked not only with, but sometimes even for, his students. Some were Americans, through whom (and particularly through Henry P. Bowditch who returned to teach at Harvard) Ludwig's influence became predominant in the laboratory teaching of physiology in America in the late nineteenth century. In contrast the outstanding characteristic of both Magendie's and Bernard's teaching was their brilliant demonstrations before their classes rather than their direction of laboratory work.

Bernard questioned his American visitors on the work on gastric juice of their fellow countryman, Dr. William Beaumont. Dr. Willis Green Edwards wrote to Beaumont of Bernard's curiosity about what had finally happened to the famous patient with the gastric fistula, Alexis Saint-Martin. Beaumont's reply reporting the continued well-being of his patient was forwarded by Edwards to Bernard and found its way into a lecture in June, 1855.

Another American doctor, Francis Donaldson, wrote home to Maryland an account of the researches on the digestive juices demonstrated when he attended Bernard's lectures in 1851:

> It was curious to see walking about the amphitheater of the College of France dogs and rabbits, unconscious contributors to science, with five or six orifices in their bodies from which at a moment's warning, there could be produced any secretion of the body, including that of the several salivary glands, the stomach, the liver, and the pancreas.

Dr. Silas Weir Mitchell, who was to become the founder of neurology in America and attain fame for his "rest cure", the treatment of functional neuroses by prolonged rest, and for his novels and verse, was also in Paris as a young man during 1850 and 1851. He recorded:

> I took courses designed for surgical training, but I liked better the lessons of Bernard in physiology and Robin in microscopy. I recall one remark of Bernard's. I said, "I think so and so must be the case." "Why think," he replied, "when you can experiment. Exhaust experiment, and then think."

This sounds more like Magendie than Bernard, but Bernard may have modeled himself pedagogically on his old teacher. A resistance to the rationalizing approach in science was often expressed in the late eighteenth and early nineteenth centuries. John Hunter wrote to Edward Jenner, "But why think? Why not try the experiment?"

All the Americans were greatly impressed by the use of living animals at the College of France, being unaccustomed to this method of teaching physiology. John Call Dalton, who visited Paris in 1850, made the claim after he was appointed to the chair of physiology in the College of Physicians and Surgeons in New York, that he was the first in America to use vivisection in his demonstrations.

The best remembered group of Bernard's English students, George Harley, William Pavy, and John Scott Burdon-Sanderson, were in Paris in 1851 and 1852. Pavy and Burdon-Sanderson seem to have been treated more like research students, carrying out their own experiments under Bernard's direction, Pavy working on sugar estimation in the blood and Burdon-Sanderson on pancreatic secretion. After their return, the three young men dominated the teaching of physiology in London.

It would be difficult to guess from Bernard's writings, or from most of what has been written about him, that the Paris of 1848 to 1851 had been very stormy politically. He had arrived in the capital too late to witness the disorders of 1830 which accompanied the deposition of the reactionary Charles X and the succession of Louis Philippe. However, in February, 1848, when Louis Philippe was in his turn dethroned, a mob attacked the Tuilleries and invaded the Assembly, crying, "Down with the Bourbons, old and new! Long live the Republic!" The Second French Republic had a short but stirring life. In June, 1848, the year of its inauguration, just a month after Bernard and his friends had met to found the Society of Biology, the Social Democrats led an insurrection which culminated in a three-day battle in the streets of Paris, in which more than ten thousand persons were killed. By the end of 1851 a general feeling that a strong hand was needed led to the election as President of Louis Napoleon, nephew of Napoleon Bonaparte, and a year later to his establishment of the Second Empire, "by the grace of God and the will of the people," in the phrase of the official proclamation. Bernard, unlike Magendie, seems to have had no pronounced republican and liberal leanings. Indeed, he had no expressed political interests whatever at this stage of his career. His mild conservatism blossomed in the congenial atmosphere of the Second Empire's last few years.

The only fragment of information about his personal life in the early 1850's is that his third child, a daughter, Marie Louise Alphonsine, was born May 14, 1850. This little girl never appears except, as it were, in attendance upon her more assured sister Tony. There is also a photograph belonging to the year 1850 of Bernard's mother in a white cap arranged, not without coquetry, over ringlets, with her grand-daughter Tony, aged three, on her knee. We know that Mme. Pierre Bernard in her whole life never came to Paris. It is likely that Claude Bernard's family shared with him his annual country holiday at Saint-Julien in 1850.

7

CURARE: MUSCLE CONTRACTION INDEPENDENT OF NERVE STIMULUS (1849–1852)

However, I could get from the earlier observations no guiding idea about the mechanism of death by curare. . . . Therefore . . . I made experiments to see *things about which I had absolutely no preconceived idea.* Introduction to the Study of Experimental Medicine.

CHRONICLING BERNARD'S EXPERIMENTAL ACTIVITIES BETWEEN 1846 and 1857 becomes increasingly like an attempt to describe what is going on in all three rings of a circus at once. We have seen how his work on the pancreas and the liver overlapped in time. During 1849 and 1850, while he was completing his demonstration of the liver as the source of blood sugar, we find him resuming the study which he had begun in 1844 of the effects of the South American poison curare.

For fifty years the poison had interested explorers, chemists, and pharmacologists but no explanation had been offered of the mechanism by which it brought such speedy death. Bernard had no theory in mind when he began his experiments, and in his *Introduction* chose his researches on curare to illustrate investigation begun without the guiding light of an hypothesis. In his own words, "we experiment to bring to birth observations which may in turn bring to birth ideas." He added, recalling Bacon's comparison, that there were cases where the hunter "instead of waiting quietly for game, tries to make it rise by beating up the locality where he assumes it may be hidden."

Bernard may have regarded working with curare almost as a form of relaxation. He acquainted himself with all the explorers' stories about the poison, beginning with Sir Walter Raleigh at the end of the sixteenth century and continuing into the early 1800's which saw the expeditions of Charles Waterton and Alexander von Humboldt. He obtained direct information about the preparation of the poison by natives from South American friends of Pelouze and Magendie. He was also interested in the earthenware jars used by the Indians to store the poison and in the forms of their arrows. Setting out to disentangle fact from legend he confidently expected that "the truth, when it was found, would be quite as marvelous as the romantic creations of the imagination."

When he had first tried the poison on a frog, in 1844, it turned limp and flabby in seven minutes, and pinching the skin no longer produced any reaction. An immediate autopsy revealed a heart still beating and the blood apparently normal, but electric stimulation of the nerves provoked no muscular movements, although, when directly stimulated, the muscles contracted vigorously. This indicated that the action of curare, like that of other poisons, was selective. It seemed to affect nerve but not muscle. The continued beating of the heart could be accounted for because heart muscle has the property of automatically rhythmic contraction without nerve stimulus, whereas skeletal muscle normally contracts only on stimulation from its motor nerve.

What interested Bernard when he returned to the subject in 1849 was the mode of entry of the poison. Its use in the chase suggested that it was fatal when introduced into the blood stream but harmless when taken into the stomach, since the game killed with curare could be eaten with impunity. Yet the poison was not destroyed by the digestive juices since, if curare was introduced into the stomach of a dog (which suffered no consequent inconvenience), an instrument dipped in its gastric juice produced a fatal wound as readily as one dipped in unmixed curare. The poison was not absorbed through the mucus membrane of the stomach unless present in great concentration or unless the animal was fasting.

In October, 1850, he reported with Pelouze to the Academy of Sciences a refinement of his 1844 experiment. He inserted dry curare under the skin of the back of a frog, and as soon as the effects of the poison were evident, removed the skin to expose the motor nerves to the hind legs. Electrical stimulation of these nerves produced no contraction in the hind legs but direct stimulation of the muscles produced vigorous contraction. This experiment furnished proof of the independent excitability of muscle, a matter of debate since Albrecht von Haller had distinguished between irritability, meaning the power of living muscle to contract, and sensitivity, the property peculiar to nerves of conveying impulses. The question, can muscle contract independently of its nerve, was now answered in the affirmative. Bernard further showed that stimulation of the vagi, which normally stops the beating of the heart, did not have this effect if curare had been administered.

The independence of the property of muscular contraction from the normal nerve stimulus is a less academic consideration than might at first appear. Modern therapy for infantile paralysis is based upon it. Massage and exercise of the paralyzed muscles aim at preserving their contractility until the destroyed nerves grow back into the muscle. Unexercised muscle, deprived of its nerves, atrophies into mere connective tissue without the power to contract.

The outstanding characteristic of death by curare had seemed to be its quietness, the absence of suffering for the victim. Bernard repeats Waterton's description of the death of an Indian hunter whose poison-tipped arrow, shot upwards into a tree had missed a monkey in the branches and, falling, had pierced the hunter's arm. Resigned to his fate, the Indian removed the little bamboo box containing the poison which was suspended from his shoulder, and putting it on the ground with his bow and arrow, stretched himself beside them to await death, which came quickly. Birds in flight, pierced by tiny, needle-sharp arrows launched from a blowpipe, seemed not to feel the wound, but after a moment dropped without a flutter. A wild boar, receiving a poisoned arrow in the jaw, did not pause in its rush, but dropped after covering a hundred yards.

Bernard also described the action of the poison on a laboratory animal:

> A puppy, pricked on the thigh with a poisoned instrument, scarcely noticed the wound; it ran and leapt as usual, but at the end of three or four minutes the animal lay down on its belly as if it were tired; it retained all its intelligence and did not seem to suffer at all; it was merely disinclined to move. Soon the dog put its head on the ground between its two front feet, as if it were still more tired and would like to go to sleep. Nevertheless, its eyes were still open and peaceful while its body

> collapsed; the animal was then completely paralyzed. Soon its eyes became dull, its respiratory movements ceased, and the animal was dead eight minutes after the poisoned prick.

The observation that death actually resulted from suffocation was not new. Waterton and Brodie in 1815 had administered curare to a donkey, and after its apparent death, had made an incision in the windpipe and carried on artificial respiration by means of a pair of bellows inserted in the opening over a period of two hours. When the animal revived sufficiently to lift its head, the bellows were stopped, and it collapsed again. However, after the artificial respiration had been resumed for another two hours, the donkey recovered completely.

In 1852 Bernard gave his experiment on the frog the final form which revealed the realities of death by curare. He ligatured the blood vessels going to one of the hind legs, being careful to leave the sciatic nerve intact, before inserting curare under the skin of the back. The poison was thus prevented from reaching the one leg below the ligature. He found that he could not only obtain a reflex response by pinching the unpoisoned limb, but could also get a response from this limb by pinching the skin on the parts of the animal subjected to the influence of the poison. Elaborating this experiment, he ligatured both legs, and found that by pinching the nose of the curarized frog, he could make it push its inert body through water with the unparalyzed hind legs. He concluded that curare did not act upon the nervous system as a whole. The sensory nerves remained unaffected while the motor nerves were prevented from conveying a normal stimulus to the muscles, which retained their excitability. It is now held that the blockade occurs at the neuromuscular junction, and Bernard himself in 1867 said that curare attacked the nervous fiber at the peripheral and not the central extremity.

The peacefulness of death by curare is an illusion in the light of this explanation of how it comes about. The victim is not deprived of sensation or intelligence, but only of the means of expressing these by movement. Speech disappears first, then movements of the limbs, then those of the face and chest, and last of all those of the eyes. Death comes when the nerve-controlled respiratory muscles cease to act. The beating of the heart, which is not dependent upon nerve stimulus, continues, but the blood which it sends around the body is no longer oxygenated and the animal dies of asphyxiation. Bernard described the plight of the sufferer:

> Can we imagine a more horrible fate than that of an intelligence watching the progressive loss of all the organs . . . which are destined to serve it, and finding itself shut up still living in a corpse? All down the ages, poetic fiction has sought to awaken our pity by representing living creatures locked in inanimate bodies. Our imagination cannot conceive of anything more wretched than that sensitive beings, who feel pleasure and pain, should be unable to seek one and avoid the other. The suffering which the imaginations of poets have invented is produced in nature by the action of the American poison. We can even say that fiction falls short of reality. When Tasso describes Clorinda imprisoned alive in a majestic cypress, at least he left her tears and sobs to complain and soften those who made her suffer by injury to the bark which could feel.

As time went on, Bernard carried out many experiments on dosage and the progressive action of the poison. These indicated that a small dose produced only the earlier effects of a large dose; therefore a less than fatal dose would produce paralysis of the limbs but not of the respiratory muscles. This is the starting point of the use of curare as a drug. The physiologist uses it to quiet muscular movement in anesthetized animals, often in combination with artificial respiration; the surgeon uses it as an adjuvant with anesthesia, *e.g.*, to relax the body wall in abdominal operations. A more recent use is to protect patients from injury in the convulsions occurring in shock therapy. The earliest therapeutic use of curare, still approved, was to control convulsions in tetanus.

Bernard applied his findings on dosage to accidental curare poisoning. The obvious expedients of immediate amputation or prolonged artificial respiration (when the iron lung was yet to come) were unnecessarily drastic. If the wound was in a limb, the first thing to do was to put a ligature above it. This would prevent the poison being conveyed in the blood stream to the heart, and from there throughout the circulatory system. But how could the poison be got rid of? He proposed that the poison be released in small doses by loosening the ligature and tightening it again as soon as the earliest paralysis appeared, repeating the procedure when recovery from paralysis showed that the released poison had been eliminated in the urine. Where the wound could not be ligatured, Bernard would have tried artificial respiration, but later research has devised satisfactory antidotes for curare poisoning, and the use of curare clinically has been attended by a mortality of practically zero.

Bernard was fascinated by curare as "an instrument which dissociates and analyzes the most delicate phenomena of the living mechanism." This is the metaphor of an anatomist, and we are reminded that he made his debut in physiology by placing his natural skill in dissection at

8

VASOMOTOR NERVES; ACADEMIC ACTIVITIES; GLYCOGENESIS (1851–1855)

The observation which I had just made was new; but the experiment itself was not. It was more than a century old. Animal Heat.

IN OCTOBER, 1851, BERNARD ANNOUNCED TO THE SOCIETY OF Biology that upon cutting the sympathetic nerve in the neck of the rabbit, he had observed the side of the head where the nerve had been cut becoming warmer than the other side, the ear in particular flushing and showing a network of enlarged blood vessels. In his audience was Brown-Séquard, who in a few months was to leave for America, since he had taken a small part in the armed protest against Louis Napoleon's coup d'état at the end of 1851.

This operation of cutting the sympathetic nerve in the neck had been performed as early as 1727 by Pourfour du Petit, a physician, who had observed that it resulted in constriction of the pupil of the eye. He had not noticed the effect on temperature, nor had any of the other experimenters who had repeated his operation. Bernard himself had cut the nerve to demonstrate constriction of the pupil many times without noticing the change in temperature.

This was the first step in his discovery of the nervous control of the blood vessels. He made a second report of it to the Academy of Sciences in March, 1852. His attention was concentrated on the temperature change, although he noted the engorged state of the blood vessels. He did not think that the rise in temperature was fully accounted for by the increased circulation, because it was more persistent than the dilation of the larger vessels. He was curiously stubborn about accepting what seemed to others the simple explanation that relaxation of the blood vessels from nervous control would account for increased temperature.

In December, 1853, before the Society of Biology, he reviewed the history of earlier work on cutting the sympathetic nerve in the neck, especially the recent contribution of Budge and Waller, awarded the prize in experimental physiology for 1852. All the other experimenters, he said, had concentrated their attention on the phenomena in the eye; he alone had observed the alteration in temperature. He was indignant over the suggestion by Budge and Waller that their work had *implied* his discovery. He went on to describe fully the results of section of the sympathetic nerve which included: (1) rise in temperature and increased circulation on the operated side; (2) constriction of the pupil; (3) drooping of the upper eyelid; (4) recession of the eye into the orbit. This response is now known as either Horner's, or the Horner-Bernard, syndrome, because Horner in 1869 was the first to describe it for man.

Bernard further stated that during his lecture demonstrations in the summer of 1852 he had stimulated the upper cut end of the sympathetic nerve by means of galvanism, and had in this way reversed the effects of cutting it. The skin became pale and the circulation enfeebled. When the stimulation ceased, the phenomena resulting from cutting the nerve returned, and the effects could be alternated almost indefinitely.

He concluded his paper by remarking that Brown-Séquard, who had just returned from America, had told him that while in that country *he* had tried the experiment of galvanizing the cut end of the nerve and had observed the consequent cooling of the parts and the contraction of the blood vessels of the face and ear. Having published his observation in the Philadelphia *Medical Examiner* for August, 1852, he considered that he had actually been first to perform this part of the experiment. Bernard's comment was a little dry:

> I shall not enter upon discussion of priority with regard to facts which all date from the same year, and which developed immediately as natural corollaries of my first experiment. I merely congratulate myself on the eagerness with which the experimenters mentioned above have followed me in the study of these phenomena of animal heat. It convinces me that they regard my findings as important and worthy of their interest.

It is only fair to add that Brown-Séquard did relate the change in temperature directly to paralysis of the arteries consequent upon their being deprived of their nerve supply, and Waller was of the same opinion. It was long before Bernard made grudging concessions on this point, and meanwhile he had approached the problem by a different path. The Academy of Sciences supported his claim to having made an original contribution in this work by awarding him in 1853, for the fourth and last time, their prize in experimental physiology.

Magendie resigned all the lectures at the College of France to Bernard at the end of 1852. The old professor wrote to the administration complaining that his quarters were airless, while the dampness in the laboratory had given his substitute painful rheumatism. This is the first suggestion that Bernard's health was not proving equal to the demands of his laborious life. On February, 1853, Magendie wrote again requesting that 1,000 francs be found for Bernard out of the 1852 budget, but whether as additional compensation or an unpaid balance is not clear. The terms of his recommendation were that Bernard had "performed inestimable services in my laboratory."

After two previous unsuccessful attempts to secure a seat for Bernard in the Academy of Sciences, he was finally elected in 1854. Membership in this Academy, one of five composing the Institute of France, is limited to sixty-six and vacancies are created only by death. Bernard had applied when a vacancy occurred in 1850, but was not even nominated. In 1852, although he did not apply, his name was brought up by the nominating committee; but he was not elected. In 1854, on the death of Roux, a member of the section of medicine and surgery, Bernard again applied. This time his name was put first by the nominating committee, and he received 42 out of 51 votes. Magendie was chairman of the nominating committee, and it is said that Longet, who had also applied, when he realized the combination he was facing, withdrew from the contest. The imperial decree approving Bernard's election was dated July 1, 1854; it was therefore just before his forty-first birthday that he received this official recognition of his eminence as a scientist in France.

Bernard's academic activities were extended in 1854 by his appointment to a newly created chair of general physiology in the Faculty of Sciences at the Sorbonne. His presentation of a thesis the year before to qualify for the degree of Doctor of Natural Sciences may have been preparatory to this appointment. One of the two chairs of botany at the Sorbonne had become vacant, and the new chair in physiology was created in its place. Dr. Rayer had been instrumental in bringing this about with Bernard in view. The new professorship increased Bernard's income by about 7,000 francs a year.

Bernard's lectures at the Sorbonne seem to have been less well received than those he gave at the College of France. According to P. E. L. van Tieghem, later Bernard's biographer, who heard him at the Sorbonne, he was a mediocre lecturer, ill at east before an audience. Van Tieghem conceded that the problems discussed were of great importance and the solutions arrived at impressive. An auditor at the College of France in 1853 commented: "Everyone knows with what eagerness pupils flock to this young and eminent professor." It is likely that Bernard was handicapped at the Sorbonne by not being able to accompany his lectures by demonstrations. A modern parallel might be made with the dependence of some lecturers upon the darkened auditorium and the illustrative slide. Bernard's request for a laboratory at the Sorbonne in connection with his professorship had to wait ten years. In 1864 he was granted funds for a *préparateur,* and was able to install a favorite pupil, Paul Bert.

Bernard very early began the formal publication of his lectures following the precedent set by Magendie. Before they were printed in France, however, a series on blood, given in the winter of 1853–1854, was published in English, in the United States, with Bernard's permission, from notes taken by a young American physician, Walter F. Atlee. The close relation of Bernard's lectures to his researches is illustrated by accounts of the production of sugar in the liver and the recent experiments on the sympathetic nerves. We learn that Magendie was among those who were satisfied that increased circulation accounted for the rise in temperature in the rabbit's ear, while Bernard still held that there were "circumstances which make this explanation a difficult one." Dr. Atlee's notes read:

> M. Bernard will show hereafter that the mechanism of these phenomena is active and not passive, and that the blood is warmer when it leaves the part than when it entered, and the effect is upon the capillaries, the large vessels being simply elastic tubes, and but indirectly affected by the experiment.

The one part of this pronouncement which holds a germ of the truth is the reference to the capillaries, if this expression may be taken as referring loosely to the smallest visible blood vessels, which are, in fact, not capillaries, but arteries and veins. The warmth in the rabbit's ear is due to the volume and rapidity of blood flow in these small vessels, rather than to increased content of the larger vessels.

The first set of lectures published in France, the winter course of 1854–1855, centered around Bernard's major discovery, the glycogenic function of the liver. The terms *matière glycogène* (sugar-forming substance), *glycogénique,* and *glycogénie,* now part of the vocabulary of the subject, were coined for use in these lectures.

An even more important innovation in language (although its application to the liver was not precise) was his use of the term "internal secretion," which now defines a whole separate province of physiology. He wished to distinguish between two secretory functions of the liver. The bile secreted in the liver and conveyed outside it into the upper end of the intestine by the bile duct may be regarded as an external secretion. The sugar-forming substance, which releases sugar (in the energy-producing form of glucose) from the liver into the blood, Bernard regarded as an internal secretion. He later mentioned the thyroids and adrenals as glands with similar internal secretions. His general term has been adopted, and the thyroid and adrenals are conspicuous among the endocrines or organs of internal secretion. The term has now a narrower significance than that which Bernard first gave it. An internal secretion, or hormone, is one liberated from a ductless gland and transmitted to another part of the organism where it performs an excitatory or depressive function, but has little or no value as a source of energy. The liver is regarded rather as an organ adapted for the storage and liberation of carbohydrate, the principal source of energy for the body.

In Bernard's simile the liver was like a syringe filled with sugar, which injected its contents at need into the blood stream. In the healthy animal the amount was regulated so that there was no surplus over physiological requirements to be eliminated in the urine. The appearance of sugar in the urine was a symptom of diabetes and of a failure of the internal equilibrium. The notion of the existence in living organisms of regulating processes which result in the maintenance of "dynamic equilibrium" was one which Bernard himself was to develop and which he bequeathed to physiologists of a later generation. Sir Ernest Starling of University College, London, who with Sir William Bayliss discovered the hormone evoking pancreatic secretion, in the early 1900's used as a lecture title the phrase "the wisdom of the body" to convey the idea of harmonious regulation of bodily functions. Walter B. Cannon of Harvard gave the expression wide currency when he used it as the title of his book describing the researches on the sympathetic nervous system in which he elaborated Bernard's basic conception.

Bernard concluded his course of lectures by referring to experiments of other physiologists which confirmed or questioned his conclusions. He accepted the confirmatory experiments but considered the others open to criticism of method. He insisted that the formation of sugar in the liver was "no longer a matter for debate"; it was "a physiological truth perfectly established and completely in the possession of science." Still he was himself to have the opportunity of making assurance doubly sure.

It was in the early autumn of 1855 that he announced the new experiment. His summer lectures on the salivary glands and the pancreas had been prepared by two pupils, Lefèvre and Tripier, for publication along with the winter lectures on the liver as Volumes I and II of *Lectures on Experimental Physiology Applied to Medicine.* Bernard's work in the laboratory seems still to have been concerned with the liver. He was carrying out analyses to compare the amounts of sugar in the livers of animals in varying conditions of nutrition and health. To check their accuracy, these analyses of liver tissue were done in duplicate. Once, not having time to complete both analyses he left the second until the following day. When he performed it, he found to his dismay an amount of sugar greatly in excess of that shown in the analysis of the night before. He reflected:

> What was I to do? Should I consider these two discordant analyses a bad experiment and disregard them? Should I take an average between the two results? . . . But that is a method of which I do not approve. . . . What was the reason which had made me find two such different values in the analysis of my rabbit's liver? After having made sure that there was no error in the method of the analysis, after noting that all parts of the liver were practically equally rich in sugar, there remained only the time which elapsed between the animal's death and my second analysis. Without attaching much importance to it, up to that time I had carried out my experiments a

> few hours after the animal's death; now for the first time I found myself in the situation of making one analysis a few minutes after death, and postponing the other until the next day, *i.e.,* twenty-four hours later. In physiology, questions of time are always very important, because organic matter undergoes great and constant variation. Some chemical change might therefore have taken place in the liver tissue.

Bernard then made a series of comparative analyses of liver tissue taken immediately after death and at the end of various periods of time, and satisfied himself that the sugar content of the liver increased on standing. He varied the experiment by attaching a hose to the portal vein of a freshly removed and still warm liver and flushing it with cold water for forty minutes. At the end of this time the copper-salt test indicated that no sugar remained in the liver tissue. But when the washed liver was kept at a mild temperature for a few hours or until the next day, the tissue and the liquor which had seeped out of it were once again found to be rich in sugar. He now felt that he had absolute proof that sugar was produced in the liver "at the expense of a substance residing in the recesses of its tissues." He was sure also that the substance was insoluble, since it had survived the prolonged washing to which he had subjected the organ. The next step, obviously, was to isolate this substance, but, foreseeing that the process would be a long one, Bernard was content, September 24, 1855, to submit to the Academy of Sciences his results so far under the title, "On the Mechanism of the Formation of Sugar in the Liver."

Since 1852 when he had ceased to lecture at the College of France, Magendie had steadily lost ground in health. He came less frequently to the Academy of Sciences, convinced that its faulty ventilation increased his shortness of breath. He clung to his chairmanships of committees, but for the most part now spent his time at his country home outside Paris at Sannois. It was probably just after the announcement to the Academy of his culminating experiment on the liver that Bernard went to call upon Magendie at Sannois. The old professor knew that his days were numbered, and told Bernard that he wished, so far as it was in his power, to bequeath to his most distinguished pupil his chair of medicine at the College of France. He added, with characteristic wry humor, "At least it won't be going to a mollycoddle."

On October 7, 1855, the day after his seventy-second birthday, Magendie died. On December 17 the Academy sent its recommendation to the Minister of Education that Bernard succeed Magendie and the choice was duly approved. The December lectures seem to have been postponed, for it was February 29, 1856, when Bernard opened his first course as Professor of Medicine with the words: "Since our last meeting in this place we have lost Magendie, one of the glories of French medicine and physiology."

What Bernard found to say in this lecture of the man of whom he speaks in the French manner as "my master," is testimony to his profound respect for the older man's intellectual distinction and the contribution he had made to physiology and medicine, especially through his sponsorship of the experimental method. It also bore witness to an understanding which had come gradually and in spite of the difficulties created by Magendie's idiosyncrasies. When Bernard speaks of a young man, "full of youthful ardor," encountering in Magendie an almost brutal skepticism toward the value of his ideas and the quality of his work, we can see, through a very thin disguise, Bernard himself in his first years as research assistant. It is his own hard-won victory that he describes:

> Magendie liked people to show him the deference which was naturally due to his high position, but he did not like weakness. One had to be able to stand up to him sometimes, and he liked a man to maintain his independence of mind, just as he insisted on it for himself. It was on these terms that one could win and keep his esteem and friendship.

Bernard was fully conscious of the value of the apprenticeship which he had served under Magendie. Their association was fruitful because they were so unlike, although both (Bernard at once and Magendie in due time) recognized in each other the marks of sheer intelligence. Bernard was by nature imaginative and intuitive. Magendie was skepticism incarnate. When Bernard had learned to accept the negatively critical standards of Magendie, which referred every imaginative flight or rationalization back to reality, he was equipped with the balance of intuitive and critical power which is perhaps the most general characteristic of the scientific (or indeed any other first-rate) mind. His natural integrity made him willing to submit to any discipline of which he recognized the usefulness.

He was especially proud to be numbered in the legacy of experimenters which Magendie had bequeathed to physiology. Before Magendie, Bernard said, the experimenters could be counted; after him, it was the physiologists who did not experiment who could be counted and who needed to justify their existence. Although he did not say so, he was the experimenter *par excellence,* whose natural genius had responded to the best in Magendie. It was in every way appropriate that the succession at the College of France should now pass to him formally, as it had been his in reality since at least 1852.

9

COMPLETION AND CONSOLIDATION OF THE MAJOR DISCOVERIES (1856–1859)

It is to experiment on the living animal that final reference must always be made to reach an understanding of organic properties. Memoir on the Pancreas.

BERNARD TOOK HIS DUTIES AT THE COLLEGE OF FRANCE WITH the utmost seriousness. He regarded the chair of medicine there as a unique institution because it represented, he said, the aspect of medical science in which at any given time the greatest progress was being made. He considered this borne out by the widely differing interests of his predecessors since the foundation of the chair in 1542. The most recent incumbents, Corvisart (1794) and Laennec (1822), had both been clinicians, but the former had introduced the practice of percussion from Vienna in his instruction in Internal Medicine, and the latter had made brilliant studies in diagnosis of diseases of the heart and lungs. When Magendie came to the chair it was as the representative of physiology, the new growing point of medical progress.

With Bernard this period reached its zenith. He therefore did not regard his professorship as an encroachment upon his research, but from 1855 onwards was inclined rather to direct his research in the service of his professorship. He had already presented his work on the liver and the pancreas in the first two volumes of his published lectures. He now planned extension of work he had already done, notably in regard to carbon monoxide, for the course running from March through June, 1856, on *Toxic Substances.*

The routine of keeping laboratory records and preparing Bernard's lectures for publication was well established. His almost incessant laboratory work since about 1839 had been recorded in a series of notebooks. Since work on different problems overlapped and since there were periods during which he might allow a particular problem to lie fallow, the material in these notebooks needed a good deal of sorting to make it useful for reference.

His first assistant in this work was a recent medical graduate, A. Tripier, whom Bernard speaks of as his "friend and pupil." Tripier made abstracts of the experiments recorded in Bernard's notebooks, arranging them in three classes: (1) those to be supplemented by further experiment; (2) those suitable for current lectures; (3) those which might fill out omissions in lectures already given but not yet published.

Bernard kept a supervisory eye upon Tripier's activities, and from time to time dictated notes giving new form to some of the exposition or outlining a new piece of research or an idea for a fresh course of lectures. He continued to keep his current laboratory notebooks, into which, it is interesting to learn, it was not his habit to enter experiments as they were performed. The notes of experiments were made on loose sheets, scrupulously dated, from which final accounts were subsequently assembled in the laboratory notebook or *cahier.*

Bernard's lectures were given from the arrangement of material arrived at between Tripier and himself. Very complete notes were taken as the lectures were delivered (Bernard in a letter promises to show a friend "the stenography of my introductory lecture"), subject to additional grooming by Tripier and final revision by Bernard himself. In connection with the posthumous publication of a lecture, Tripier remarked that he had refrained from making changes which he would have made if Bernard had been alive to approve a final version. In Bernard's lifetime he had often "altered and condensed the wording with a view to making it render . . . the parent idea."

Tripier assisted Bernard from 1854 to 1863, and after that similar duties were performed by Mathias Duval and J. F. A. Dastre. Atlee's edition of the lectures *On the Blood* perhaps comes closest to a reproduction of what actually went on in the lecture room. The official French series of *Leçons* is a more composite literary production, although the intention was to keep it faithful to Bernard's ideas and manner of teaching.

In the lectures on *Toxic Substances* Bernard dealt with poisons which attacked the organism in dissimilar ways. The subject matter lent itself to striking demonstrations. Birds immersed in hydrogen sulphide gas died instantly; but when it was injected in solution into the jugular vein of a dog (the shortest path to the lungs through the right side of the heart), the animal, unharmed, breathed the gas out to blacken a test paper held before its nose. Hydrogen sulphide produces a fatal effect only when carried to the tissues by the capillaries. Small animals placed under bell jars demonstrated that they could live longer in oxygen if the carbon dioxide produced in respiration was removed as soon as it was formed. Two substances were introduced separately, and harmlessly, into the jugular vein of a rabbit; when they were introduced together, the animal died immediately of poisoning by hydrocyanic acid formed by their combination in the alkaline medium provided by the blood.

Most important for their new physiological implications were the experiments on carbon monoxide which Bernard reported for the first time in these lectures. He showed that this gas replaces oxygen quantitatively, and makes the normal gaseous exchange between the blood and tissues thereafter impossible. Death by carbon monoxide is therefore a kind of asphyxiation. The blood in the lungs absorbs no oxygen, and the blood in the capillaries releases no oxygen for the tissues to burn to carbon dioxide.

Poisoning by carbon monoxide in the form of charcoal fumes had been discussed since the days of Erasistratus and Galen, as Bernard pointed out; but he was the first to explain its mechanism. He had no technique of resuscitation to propose if enough of the gas had been inhaled, since there was no means of reversing the chemical change in the blood. If a smaller quantity had been inhaled, the blood seemed to recover its respiratory power. In the nineteenth century danger lurked in leaky chimneys, closed flues, and open charcoal braziers; in the twentieth it reappeared in closed garages where automobile engines were left running. Bernard demonstrated that a mixed atmosphere of carbon monoxide and carbon dioxide (which would be present in cases of suicide or accidental poisoning) was more deadly than one of pure carbon monoxide. This results from the stimulation of the respiratory center by carbon dioxide. The consequent faster breathing would introduce more carbon monoxide into the lungs, and its toxic influence on the blood would take effect sooner.

Although this work on the blood was original, Bernard is not ordinarily credited with advancing our knowledge of its oxygen-carrying properties, since Hoppe-Seyler in Germany was working more intensively on this subject at the same time. The latter's observation of the effect of carbon monoxide in giving a bright red color to the blood was published in 1857. This phenomenon had also been Bernard's starting point. Hoppe-Seyler eventually made a more complete investigation of the properties of the red coloring matter of the blood, for which he proposed the name hemoglobin in 1864. When Bernard later came to know the work of his German contemporary, he spoke of it with enthusiasm to his students.

Bernard was also engaged in the early fifties on work for the completion of his *Mémoire sur le pancréas (Memoir on the Pancreas),* published at the end of 1856, a complete review of his first major discovery, the role of the pancreas in digestion. A significant addition since his last formal report in 1849 is the reference to the action of the pancreas of the fetus on neutral fats. This characteristic does not appear until a very short time before birth, an observation which gave the lead to Banting in 1921 to try to extract the hormone from the pancreas of the fetus before this gland had developed far enough to produce the digestive enzyme trypsin. The efforts of other experimenters to isolate insulin from the pancreas of the fully developed animal had been frustrated because the hormone was destroyed by trypsin. This gives Bernard a somewhat distant, but quite fundamental, connection with the discovery of the control by the pancreas of sugar production, of which he himself was never aware.

The *Memoir* aroused some of his critics, unconvinced of the digestive action of pancreatic juice on fats, to a public attack. During 1857, Bérard, professor of physiology in the faculty of medicine, claimed to have found digestion of fat in herbivores (oxen) in which the pancreatic duct had been ligated. Bernard was able to point out that Bérard had ignored the fact that there is more than one pancreatic duct in the ox, and that he had therefore not excluded all pancreatic juice from the intestine in his experiment.

At about the same time the indefatigable Longet in references to Bernard's work on the pancreas in a textbook, not only questioned the value of the work but hinted that it had been anticipated by a German investigator, Eberle, as early as 1834. Bernard showed that Eberle had never worked with pancreatic juice at all, but with a liquid which was, by his own statement, acid, *i.e.,* without the fundamental alkalinity of the pancreatic secretion. In a lecture a year later, Bernard ironically remarked that Longet seemed bent upon establishing that his experiments were worthless, and at the same time that Eberle had anticipated him. It was very difficult, he thought, to reconcile these points of view. If Eberle's experiments were good and he had merely repeated them, his must be good too. If his experiment proved nothing, how, on Longet's hypothesis, could Eberle's views have any weight? He concluded that Longet's position could only be that if the experiments were good, they must be Eberle's, and if bad, Bernard's.

In March, 1857, Bernard announced to the Society of Biology that he had finally succeeded in isolating glycogen from liver tissue and preparing it in pure form. He had been working on the problem at intervals for a year and a half, part of the time in unfruitful collaboration with the chemist Berthelot. Pierre Mauriac relates[1] that Bernard remarked one day to Berthelot, "You made me lose three years over your formulae before I discovered glycogenesis." Bernard himself began with the observa-

[1] *Nouvelles rencontres: Amitiés de savants.* Paris, Grasset, 1930.

tion that the filtrate of an extract of liver tissue was not clear but opalescent. Alcohol produced a white precipitate, which, when dried and remoistened, gave the test for sugar. This procedure is still followed. With the assistance of Pelouze, he gave an analysis of the physical and chemical properties of the substance, which he described as an "animal starch." As it happened, Hensen in Germany had independently isolated glycogen a year earlier, in 1856. Bernard seems not to have been aware of Hensen's work, which had, of course, been undertaken in consequence of the publication of the liver-washing experiment of 1856.

There were skeptics about the glycogenic function of the liver as well as about the digestive function of the pancreas. Longet had not failed to enter a protest. In 1855 he had published an article supporting the old view of the chemists that "the sugar of the animal organism comes exclusively from plants." Bernard had intended to ignore this on the ground that it "had nothing to do with physiology," but some of his students, aware perhaps of his relations with Longet, insisted upon bringing the matter up. Thus baited, Bernard expressed with measured scorn his opinion of an author who said that he did not *like* the idea of the animal economy needlessly fabricating a substance merely to break it down again, and who thought that organic secretion was not intermittent. The "fundamental experiment" of killing a fasting dog and taking samples of blood (1) from the portal vein below a ligature cutting it off from the liver and (2) from the hepatic veins was performed before the eyes of the class. Once more Bernard demonstrated that the copper-salt test was negative for the blood from the portal vein, and definitely positive for the blood from the hepatic veins.

Longet, however, was not alone. Bernard's English pupil, William Pavy, who had worked on sugar estimation in Bernard's laboratory in 1851–1852, went home unconvinced that a normal healthy liver could produce sugar. The liver-washing experiment was not significant to him since the sugar was produced after the death of the animal. Bernard retorted that logic would demand that Pavy "consider the diabetic patient as a walking corpse, certainly a bizarre conception."

A better grounded critic was Guillaume Louis Figuier, who claimed to have found sugar in the portal vein of a meat-fed dog if the blood were taken two to four hours after a meal. Figuier was invited to repeat his experiments before a committee of the Academy of Sciences during 1855. Bernard asked to be excused from serving when his own results were in question, and the Academy members appointed were the chemists Dumas and Pelouze and Dr. Rayer. This committee upheld Bernard's position that there was no sugar in the portal vein, but admitted in its report that it had insisted on the use of a fermentation test, although Figuier's original observation had been based on a test with "Frommherz's reagent." Shortly afterwards Figuier resigned from his assistant professorship of chemistry at the Paris School of Pharmacy.

Still another experimenter, J. B. A. Chauveau, presented his results on the presence of sugar in the blood in 1856. Chauveau's main contention was that there was some sugar in all circulating blood, and less in venous than in arterial blood. He did not wish to contest Bernard's discoveries, and had himself found *more* sugar in the blood of the hepatic veins than in that of the portal. Bernard later repeated and confirmed Chauveau's results, but does not seem to have been worried by the consideration that blood enters the liver from the hepatic arteries as well as from the portal vein, and that the arteries in consequence might bring sugar to the liver. He was sure that sugar was manufactured and stored in the liver.

Nevertheless, Figuier and Chauveau were both justified in contending that there is some sugar in the blood of the portal vein. Bernard's method of sugar estimation could show the presence of sugar only in concentration above the normal fasting level. His experiment involving the ligature of the portal vein therefore did not give the clean-cut result which he believed it did. The best modern methods establish a slight but constant difference in the sugar content of blood entering and leaving the liver. Bernard, however, reported such enormously larger differences that we must seek an explanation going beyond the mere inadequacy of his sugar tests. His own demonstration of piqûre, or artificial diabetes by puncture of the floor of the fourth ventricle, suggests an explanation. His method of killing his animals was transection of the spinal cord, with consequent stimulation of all the nerve tracts in it. This stimulation would readily lead to effects on the nervous system, which in turn would cause the release of liver glycogen as glucose. It was these abnormal quantities of released sugar which Bernard measured in blood drawn from the hepatic vein.

There is disillusionment in recognizing how much instinctive judgment and even sheer luck contributed to a discovery which Bernard, with a good deal of justification, believed to be based upon the strictest experimental proof. Figuier and Chauveau have passed unhonored and unsung, but in their small way they were quite right. Bernard was transgressing his own reiterated principles in saying more than that *his method* failed to show any sugar in the portal vein. However, although his experimental data are open to criticism, all physiologists today accept his general position that carbohydrate is stored as glycogen in the liver to be released into the blood stream as glucose.

In the same year in which he was working on the isolation of glycogen, 1856, Bernard returned to the problem of where in the body sugar is destroyed, or burned to produce energy. He had never accepted Magnus's analysis of the relations of oxygen to carbon dioxide in arterial and venous blood as conclusive for this problem, nor was he satisfied by his own experiment with Magendie on the temperature of the blood in the two sides of the heart.

He enlisted the aid of François Walferdin, whom he regarded as especially competent in the technique of temperatures, and they found that blood entering the heart from the body was always a fraction of a degree warmer than blood entering it from the lungs. He further found that blood leaving the liver was warmer than blood entering it, and also that during digestion blood was warmed on traversing the intestine. His conclusion corroborated that of Magnus, that the chemical phenomena which result in heat production take place in the tissues where they are in contact with the blood. This, taken together with his account of the production of sugar in the organism, established the main points of the doctrine of carbohydrate metabolism which is still the foundation of that complicated subject.

At the end of 1856 and for the first three months of 1857 Bernard was engaged on the lectures which were to appear as the first volume of his *Leçons sur la physiologie et la pathologie du système nerveux* (*Lectures on the Physiology and Pathology of the Nervous System*). This volume includes Bernard's own account of the question of recurrent sensitivity, as it had been debated between Magendie and Longet in the early 1840's and resolved by himself in 1847. He also recorded work of his own on the spinal roots and the cord. When still an intern, he had cut the dorsal roots leading to one hind leg in a dog, and found the animal no longer able to support its weight on the desensitized limb. He elaborated the experiment now with frogs, establishing that a desensitized limb was used awkwardly and without coordination. He showed that these effects were not due merely to loss of cutaneous sensations, *e.g.,* touch, for when he denervated the *skin* of the hind legs of a frog, it swam and leapt as skilfully as usual. These experiments foreshadowed the work of Sir Charles Sherrington on the nervous mechanism responsible for coordination.

At the beginning of April, 1857, there occurred a brief and melancholy intrusion of his private life upon his absorbing scientific interests. His fourth and last child, a second son, named Claude François Henri, born January 31, 1856, died at the age of fourteen months. Tripier recalled Bernard's remark that he "now understood the upheavals in the religious ideas of those who did not feel themselves upheld by ideas of another sort." It suited Bernard to present this stoic front, but he never forgot the loss of this last son.

When he resumed his lectures he took up the functions of specific nerves, and presently we have an instance of a significant observation made for the first time in the course of an experiment before the class. He cut the chorda tympani (the small nerve which had been the subject of his first scientific paper) in the ear and saw what he had missed thirteen years earlier, *i.e.,* that the cutting of this nerve stopped salivary secretion from the submaxillary salivary gland on the same side. He also provoked secretion again by stimulating the peripheral end of the cut nerve. The chorda tympani was therefore the motor nerve to the submaxillary gland. While he was about it, he traced the source of the secretory nerve fibers of the parotid salivary gland to their origin in another cranial nerve (the small petrosal nerve). However, he still clung to the mistaken conclusion of his first paper, that the chorda tympani had nothing to do with taste.

He remarked when he reported this new work to the Society of Biology that the submaxillary gland receives its nerve supply not only from the chorda tympani, but also from the sympathetic nerve coming up from the neck. He was on the verge of the revelation of the reciprocal part played by these two nerves in the control of blood supply to the secretory gland which would complete the discovery begun with his observation of the flushed ear of a rabbit in 1851. However, the matter seems to have lain fallow in his mind for a little while. He was busy with an investigation of the elimination of various substances in the urine, probably with a view to his lectures for the coming year on *Liquids of the Organism*.

One day he made the observation destined to give birth to the experimental idea which would complete his fourth major discovery. He noticed that while the kidney was active the renal vein was filled with bright red blood, while neighboring veins had the usual dark venous blood. It occurred to him that the coloring might have a connection with the activity of the kidney, and he observed that the blood became dark when renal secretion ceased. However, as the secretion of the kidneys is almost continuous, he thought he might obtain more striking results with another gland, and at the same time establish the generality of the observation. He then exposed the submaxillary salivary gland with its veins and nerves. The gland was not secreting and its blood supply was dark. When a drop of vinegar was placed on the tongue, saliva rose in a small tube inserted into the duct of the submaxillary gland, and the color of the blood changed to bright red, its flow being at the same time more abundant. Galvanic stimulation of the chorda tympani produced the same results as the vinegar on the tongue.

The announcement of the completed discovery was made to the Academy of Sciences August 9, 1858. There were two new experiments. In the first, Bernard cut the vein of the submaxillary gland to estimate the rate of blood flow through it. He found that the drops escaped much faster during stimulation of the chorda tympani than when the gland was at rest; the blood was bright red and had a pulsatory movement. He now drew the conclusion that the dilatation of the vein resulting from the stimulation of the chorda tympani permitted the blood to enter the vein so rapidly that the arterial pulsation was not lost (*i.e.*, a venous pulse was produced). In the second experiment, he took advantage of the double nerve supply to the submaxillary gland, and by stimulating the sympathetic nerve caused the vessels to constrict, the blood flow to decrease almost to zero, and the blood itself to become dark.

His result was now perfectly clean-cut. The sympathetic nerve acts to constrict the blood vessels of the submaxillary gland, the chorda tympani to dilate them, and these actions accompany the secretory function of the gland so as to furnish an abundant blood supply during actual secretion. The action of both vasomotor and vasoconstrictor nerves had been demonstrated in a flawless experiment. The rational basis had also been provided for surgery involving a more extensive cutting of the sympathetic nerves (sympathectomy), now prescribed with varying degrees of justification for all sorts of ailments, from excessive sweating to gangrene, angina pectoris, and high blood pressure.

It is not likely that Bernard guessed this to be his last major discovery strictly in the field of animal experimentation. There is no indication that the activity in the laboratory at the College of France was in any way diminished. Plans were made for the lectures of 1857-1858 on *Liquids of the Organism.* In his introductory lecture for the winter course, Bernard made some disparaging references to the kind of investigation which consists in perfecting earlier work, adding new facts and revising details. Nevertheless, a great deal of his future activity was to be of this very kind, with the important difference that the work to be perfected was his own, and not, as in the cases criticized, someone else's. His most recent achievement had been a model of precision and completeness of demonstration, a suitable climax for his experimental record, but the historical climax was, of course, not felt at the moment, and experimentation went on as usual. Bernard himself, to judge from his rather brief account of the new work, was less impressed with it than he had been with that on the liver and the pancreas, which in some of its details was more open to criticism.

Apart from the explanation of the regulation of blood supply to the secretory organs there was little really new experimental material in the lectures on *Liquids of the Organism.* Reported perhaps for the first time was some undated work with his friend, Davaine, on "crop-milk" of pigeons. Their analysis of the avian secretion as having ingredients similar to mammalian milk, except for the lack of sugar, has been very exactly corroborated in analyses made by modern methods. The analogy between "crop-milk" and mammalian milk has been emphasized by the discovery that the same hormone from the pituitary gland stimulates both secretions. The pigeon, in consequence, is used as a convenient test animal for the lactogenic hormone, a curious bridging of the gulf between bird and mammal. Here, as so often, there can be seen in even a small piece of Bernard's work the germ of much future accomplishment.

The most interesting feature historically of *Liquids of the Organism* is that, in his discussion of the blood, Bernard uses for the first time the expression *milieu* to express an *internal* environment (*i.e.,* the blood) mediating between the life of the organism and its external environment. He was to develop this idea as time went on and coin the expression *le milieu intérieur* in direct contrast to *le milieu extérieur*. But on December 17, 1857, when he made his first recorded reference to what turned out to be a most fruitful conception, he said:

> The blood constitutes an actual organic environment intermediary between the external environment in which the complete individual lives and the living molecules which cannot safely be brought into direct contact with this external environment. Thus the blood contains all the elements necessary to life, elements which it obtains from outside by means of certain organic mechanisms. It then serves as a vehicle for all the influences which, coming from without, act upon the fibers of the tissues: oxygen, nutritive substances, temperature, etc.
>
> By means of the respiratory mechanism, the blood comes into contact with the air and obtains from it oxygen which is subsequently carried to the whole organism. By the mechanism of alimentary absorption the blood obtains from without all the liquids which are subsequently furnished to the organism to serve as nourishment for the tissues. On the other hand, all the products of organic decomposition which result from the accomplishment of the phenomena of nutrition are collected in the blood and circulate with it to be excreted, either in the form of gas through the skin and lungs or in the form of liquid by the kidneys.

Moreover, in the blood, all the tissues "are provided for the accomplishment of their functions with constant conditions of temperature, moisture, availability of oxygen, as well as nitrogenous materials, carbohydrates, and salts, without which the organs cannot be nourished." It was this concept of a controlled and constant internal environment which was to become as valuable for physiology as the doctrine of evolution, formulated at almost exactly the same time, for biology. Bernard's *Leçons sur les propriétés physiologiques et les altérations pathologiques des liquides de l'organisme* (*Lectures on the Physiological Properties and Pathological Alterations of the Liquids of the Organism*) appeared in 1859, the very year of the publication of Darwin's *On the Origin of Species by Means of Natural Selection.*

We may catch a glimpse of Bernard at this time, when he was about forty-five, through the eyes of a young student of chemistry, G. L. Jousset de Bellesme, who was one day in 1859 taken to Bernard's laboratory by Berthelot. The young man was astonished that so many discoveries could have come out of this "narrow, damp cellar." A friendship sprang up, which was strengthened when, five years later, Jousset attended Bernard's course. Jousset became professor in the medical school at Nantes, and in his fifties recalled Bernard as he had first seen him, "standing at his animal table with his tall hat on, from beneath which escaped long locks of graying hair; around his neck was a muffler which he scarcely ever took off; his shoulders were a little bent, even at his age. . . . He turned to me in a very fatherly manner, and asking me to wait a moment, went on with his experiment."

10

ENFORCED LEISURE AND REFLECTION (1859–1865)

To be a good critic, one must have settled opinions and one must have wandered in the fields of science to collect them instead of accepting them at second hand. The Red Notebook.

BETWEEN 1839 AND 1859 THERE IS NO SUGGESTION THAT Bernard maintained any interest not related, or strictly subordinated, to his life in the laboratory. His personal friendships had lasted from his student days. They still included Lasègue and Davaine who had taught with him in a girls' school to finance their earliest years of medical study. Lasègue had transferred his interest from physiology to medical practice and was regarded as a worthy follower of the great clinician Trousseau, whose pupil he had been. Davaine combined experimental interests with his practice, and was active in the Society of Biology.[1]

[1] Davaine anticipated Pasteur in observing the connection between micro-organisms and infectious disease when in 1850 he saw under the microscope what he took to be protozoa in blood taken from a sheep dead of anthrax. Pasteur paid tribute to the pioneer work of Davaine and Rayer on anthrax. An account of Davaine's work on various subjects, notably parasitology, is given by Jean Rostand, *Hommes de verité,* Stock, Paris, 1948.

Since Bernard had devoted himself altogether to physiology, the three friends illustrated the three possible solutions to the problem of their careers. Bernard also kept up his intimacy with the chemists who had collaborated with him in the early years at the College of France, Pelouze, Paul Thénard, and Barreswill. Senior to all these men was Dr. Rayer, a sort of patron saint to struggling young scientists. In his hospitable house in Paris Bernard was often to be seen.

Renan and Berthelot were his favorites among his fellow professors at the College of France. Under their influence in the late fifties he began to widen his social relations. He accompanied them every week to a dining-club meeting at the house of Jean Bouley at Passy. Bouley had taken his medical degree two years before Bernard, and his father had sat with Magendie on the Committee of Equine Hygiene. He was a successful clinician with scientific, literary, and artistic interests. The group which came to his house included the journalist Alexandre Weil, the poet and playwright Emile Deschamps, the artist Chenavard, Armand Moreau (a devoted pupil of Bernard), and Leon Renault, afterwards politically prominent. Bernard's talent for conversation is said to have been highly regarded in this circle where conversation was cultivated as one of the minor arts.

Beginning in 1862, Bernard was occasionally present at the bi-monthly dinners at the Café Magny of the literary group led by Sainte-Beuve and ornamented also by Gautier and Flaubert. When Sainte-Beuve died in 1869, Bernard wrote: "I have just learned with regret of the death of my friends Cerise and Sainte-Beuve. Two of us have gone and there will be others." Cerise was a fellow member of the Academy of Medicine.

A luncheon given by Bernard for the novelist-journalist Edmond About was rescued from oblivion when his guest drew Bernard out on the subject of rotifers with a forthcoming novel in view. Rotifers are minute creatures, living in stagnant water, which have rotatory organs for swimming and possess the capacity to survive drying, so that they come to life on being put into water again even after several years of dessication. About wanted to know if a man might not be carefully dried and later, like a rotifer, revived. From Bernard's published lectures on general physiology at the Sorbonne (*Living Tissues*) we know that he must have replied that the higher animals are unable to sustain "a latent life" with dry tissues.

About was undiscouraged, and a year or two later brought out a novel called *The Man with the Broken Ear,* in which he applied to his own purposes what he had learned about rotifers. Its hero is a French officer who is nearly frozen to death in Napoleon's Russian campaign, but is subsequently dried in vacuum by a German doctor who has been experimenting upon rotifers. Redampened after fifty years, he revives to utter a feeble "Vive l'Empereur," by that time sadly out of date. Bernard must have been entertained by the pseudo-scientific descriptions of the Colonel's mummification, slyly parodying his own style. At any rate, on the occasion of the lunch party, he radiated intelligence and good humor in the opinion of the other guests. When he began to talk, no one thought of anything but listening; his auditors were tempted to exclaim along with *le bourgeois gentilhomme* in Molière, "What a wonderful thing it is to know something."

Bernard later exercised a less accidental influence on the French novel. Zola seriously proposed to transfer the experimental procedure of science to creative writing. His theory, presented in *The Experimental Novel,* is a confused and unconvincing parody of Bernard's exposition of the experimental method in the *Introduction to the Study of Experimental Medicine,* but it had an important influence on the new "naturalistic" school of fiction. Zola even chose Bernard, "slightly and transparently disguised," as the model for his *Docteur Pascal,* although he departed radically from this plan in the final version of the novel.

Bernard kept his social and domestic life in quite separate compartments. At about the time of his appointment as Professor of Medicine at the College of France he moved to a more commodious flat at 10, rue Mogador, where he lived for eight years. His friends saw little of Mme. Bernard, and it was understood among them, although Bernard himself did not speak of the matter, that his marriage had not been a success. Pelouze, who had arranged it, said that he was grateful to Bernard for not holding it against him when things turned out as they did.

Mme. Bernard, who seems to have had a very narrow intelligence and as limited a capacity for sympathy, was unable to share or understand her husband's intellectual life. Almost the only pieces of first-hand documentary evidence about her are an account book which she kept, very meticulously, and a photograph, preserved at Saint-Julien. In the photograph she has a long, narrow face, and a long upper lip, and wears a lace cap of some elegance. The account book suggests that she was interested in money and had very little to spend. She notes at the beginning that her husband paid for his own clothes, the rent, and the "contributions," and that she received 100 francs every Monday for the housekeeping. She also received from time to time additional sums, about 100 to 400 francs a month, for purchases of material, ribbons, flowers, shoes, and schoolbooks, which she usually notes as being for one of her two daughters. Bernard's income at this time from various sources was about 1,200 to 2,000 francs a month, amounting, perhaps, to 20,000 francs a year.

A humorous light is cast on the family's life by the recurring entries of small borrowings by both Claude Bernard and Mme. Bernard from their two daughters, especially toward the end of a week. Mme. Bernard would borrow two francs to apply to the week-end chicken or to pay the floor polisher, and Bernard a few centimes for some unexplained purpose, Mme. Bernard usually making restitution on his behalf. She seems to have had a strict sense of financial integrity, and once even paid her daughters twenty-five centimes for a bite she had taken out of their three-franc easter egg. The little girls were nearly always more solvent than their parents, although they too occasionally fell into arrears over their contributions on Saints' days. There are many entries of tiny sums paid out in church collections or charities, among them a contribution of two francs to the Animal Society (or, as we say, the S.P.C.A.).

Jousset de Bellesme has spoken more frankly than any other contemporary of Bernard's relationship with his wife. In Jousset's view Mme. Bernard, irritated by the lack of common intellectual ground between herself and her husband, seized upon what she felt was the weakest point of his position and constantly upbraided him for the suffering he caused animals in his researches. These reproaches developed into a "truceless warfare."

As Jousset suggests, Mme. Claude Bernard's disapproval of her husband's use of animals in his laboratory was probably no more than a convenient weapon. Bernard did not lack sensitivity about the impression this procedure might make on those who were not scientists but he was firm in his judgment that benefits to humanity justified it. He expressed his feelings about the regrettable necessity for vivisection in a striking simile: the science of life, he said, was like a superb salon resplendent with light which one can enter only by passing through a long and ghastly kitchen.

As soon as anesthetics were introduced he began to use them in his laboratory. Sophie O'Brien, the daughter of Bernard's friend of his later years, Mme. Raffalovich, recalled that when she was a child and had to undergo an operation for adenoids, Bernard over-ruled the surgeon who wished to operate without an anesthetic and insisted on the use of chloroform.

In the differences between Bernard and his wife his friends were inclined to place the whole blame upon Mme. Bernard, because his untiring kindness, evenness of temper, and consideration were recognized by all of them. Since they took this view of Mme. Bernard, it was natural that they should avoid her house. It became the custom for the younger men especially, the growing group of "disciples," to come to the laboratory at the College of France on Mondays for conversation after the weekly meetings of the Academy of Sciences.

The steady flow of papers reporting fresh details or refinements of Bernard's principal discoveries was suddenly interrupted in March, 1860, and for two and a half years he published nothing at all. Years of incessant labor in unsanitary surroundings took their toll, and his health broke down completely. Dr. Rayer and Dr. Davaine, his personal physicians, advised a long holiday in the country. His brief vacations at the end of the summer in Saint-Julien had always been spent with his mother, who never visited him in Paris and still lived in the house where he had been born. Leaving his wife and daughters in Paris, he now went down to Saint-Julien alone.

His sojourn there was pleasant and rewarding enough to lead him to acquire a permanent country residence. In 1861 he bought from the Chevalier Lombard de Quincieux, for 60,000 francs, a house rebuilt in 1830 on the hilltop beside the Bernard farmhouse. It was a three-story stone house, covered in tawny yellow stucco, with the simple dignified lines and the low-pitched tile roof characteristic of the manor houses of the preceding century. The staircase was embellished with a fine wrought-iron railing and the de Quincieux coat-of-arms. The principal rooms, floored with red tile, had windows with a superb view across "the broad meadows of the valley of the Saône" to the distant horizon where on a clear day the "white peaks" of the Alps were just visible. The other amenities of the house are suggested in a letter inviting a friend for an overnight visit: "I can offer two bedrooms, three state beds, twelve chickens, twenty pounds of butter, a butcher and a baker in the village."

Included in the sale was a vineyard sloping down the hill from the edge of the grassy terrace bordered by a few trees in front of the house. Bernard considered this property an investment as well as a country home. Becoming a wine-grower like his forebears, he drew from it a revenue, in good years, of 8,500 francs. In 1869 he sold 170 barrels of 210 litres at 50 francs a barrel. In poor years the returns might drop to 3,000 francs.

In some sheds at the back of the house he set up an improvised laboratory, installing a few retorts for chemical analyses and collecting frogs from a neighboring swamp during afternoon walks. He worked here in the mornings. In the afternoons he busied himself with small improvements about the place, such as the bowling green he laid out on the right of the terrace. There is a story of his having had a whole wall torn down to dislodge a nest of adders. In his letters he spoke from time to time of grafting in his orchard or ordering new stock, pruning his roses, transplanting lilacs, and cultivating the violets and periwinkles of which he was particularly fond. He had an interesting collection of herbs and medicinal plants. When he visited the neighbors, they would address him in "correct" French, while he replied in the local patois.

During his long convalescence in 1861, Bernard was less inclined to activity than usual. He arranged a bench to command the view eastward to Mont Blanc and called it the bench "de Sisyphe." The pun compared his slow recovery with the unending labor of Sisyphus and described the row of six yew trees (six ifs) which stood behind the bench.

From this vantage point he liked to enjoy the sweeping expanse of country which had been shut away from his view in his childhood inside the farm courtyard. He wrote a description of this view a few years later to a friend, who lent the letter to Renan for inclusion in the latter's eulogy of Bernard before the French Academy in 1879. Renan not only "cut" some phrases, but altered others, substituting "when the sky is clear" for "when the weather is propitious" and "limitless" for "immeasurable," and editing Bernard's taste in prepositions. After speaking of an imaginary landscape stretching over the Jura mountains and Switzerland to the Alps and the Adriatic, Bernard (unedited) proceeded:

> But to remain within the limits of the visible, I see when I am at my windows or on my terrace the broad meadows of the valley of the Saône unrolling before me for a distance of five or six miles. When in the morning, for example, like today, the sun rises radiant behind majestic Mont Blanc in the distance, the Saône and its meadows are covered with haze and mist which gradually thin and dissolve. Then I can distinguish only the tops of the tall poplars and see the long snakes of smoke from the passing Paris-Lyons train, the distant rumbling of which I sometimes hear when the wind is from the east. On the hillside where I live I am surrounded by an immeasurable sea of vines, which would give the country a very monotonous appearance if it were not interrupted by shady valleys and little streams which come down from

> the mountains to the Saône. My house, although on a height, is surrounded by a nest of verdure, a little wood on the right and an orchard on the left; this is a rarity in a country where even the copses are uprooted to plant vines.

In this environment the first draft of Bernard's most famous book, the *Introduction to the Study of Experimental Medicine,* was written. The idea behind the book, however, already had a considerable history, which has been unraveled by Léon Delhoume in his recent editions of the manuscripts bequeathed by Bernard to his last *préparateur,* d'Arsonval. As early as August, 1850, Bernard had begun to assemble in a red notebook (*Le cahier rouge*) his "settled opinions." Some of the earliest of these reflections present in germinal form central ideas of the *Introduction.* The bulk of the entries in the red notebook, however, belong to 1856-1857, and it is in the following year that Bernard himself places his decision to write a general treatise on experimental medicine:

> In 1858, after having for several years given a series of lectures at the College of France on various subjects and fragmentary studies in medical physiology, I conceived the plan of a dogmatic work on experimental medicine. Unfortunately, I lacked the necessary material means and installations. Still, undiscouraged, I pressed eagerly forward in the preparation of my work, of which I published the introduction in 1865.

The lectures of 1859 and 1860, which had so far appeared only in an English translation by Benjamin Ball in the *Medical Times and Gazette,* showed the effects of this decision. They were less concerned than the earlier ones with the direct description of the principal discoveries and more with laying down broad principles of experimental practice and with placing Bernard's technical experience at the disposal of physiologists. They were in fact used later to fill in part of the unfinished design, and published as the *Experimental Pathology* of 1872, and part of the posthumous *Operative Physiology* of 1879.

The bound notebook in which Bernard first sketched the main ideas of his *Introduction,* very probably during his long stay at Saint-Julien, was exhibited on the occasion of its presentation to the College of France by Professor d'Arsonval in 1935. It is

> a humble commercial register, an account book, of the sort which might be used by a small suburban grocer. . . . The author has pasted on the cover, with a gummed postage-stamp edge, a label outlined in pen and ink with several black lines and bearing this simple inscription: *Book*. . . . On the white pages in a clear regular hand, without additions or corrections, the writer has from day to day composed his work, putting in the margin a few indications and numbers to outline a logical order.

This notebook, however, is not a full manuscript of the printed *Introduction,* but the first records of its subject matter before they were completely coordinated. It may now be assumed, from Delhoume's researches, that no such manuscript was preserved. The *Book* was in fact used for further entries, after the *Introduction* was published, as late as 1877. Delhoume has also shown in regard to another notebook that it was Bernard's practice to prepare from his notebooks a final version on loose sheets for the printer, still in his own hand. It was to such a version that Tripier referred, in all probability, when he said that the *Introduction* was completed before the end of 1862. Publication was delayed until 1865, perhaps because of revision, perhaps also because Bernard thought of this work as literally only an introduction to a definitive account of his contribution to the science which he had made so much his own.

In the summer of 1862 Bernard was encouraged by the apparent restoration of his health to return to Paris. He addressed the opening session of the Ethnographic Society early in August. A certain curiosity may be felt as to what he would choose to say to scientists in a field quite distinct from his own. He solved the problem, after some introductory remarks about the broad scope of a science devoted to the study of divisions of the human family, by a discussion of the use of poisons by primitive races, in particular, of curare. For the rest of the lecture he was on perfectly familiar ground. His peroration anticipated that the advanced science of the nineteenth century would make further discoveries among primitive peoples "who add without knowing it to their own progress along with that of civilized nations." By applying curare to the treatment of epilepsy and tetanus, he added, science had already transformed a means of death into an instrument of safety.

He appeared each week at the Academy of Sciences and presented in installments a long report on his overall researches into the relation of the sympathetic nerve to blood supply and heat production. He was appointed to a consulting Committee on Hygiene and Medical Service in the hospitals, his first mark of recognition from the bureaucracy of the Second Empire, and was promoted to the rank of Officer of the Legion of Honor.

When he looked in on his laboratory, he presumably saw at work there the Russian physiologist Ivan Michailovich Sechenov, who had obtained leave from his professorship at the Medico-Surgical Academy in St. Petersburg to work in Bernard's laboratory on an independent problem, the inhibition of reflex movements by the nervous centers. Sechenov had received his training in the principal German laboratories, especially that of Ludwig, but he may have wished to work with Bernard on his chosen problem of inhibition because of Bernard's independent observation in 1846 of the inhibitory action of the vagus nerve on the frog's heart, a year after the Weber brothers had discovered this classic phenomenon.

It is likely that Bernard's detachment from the laboratory at this time prevented his having any very close relation with Sechenov, who nevertheless stayed on and attended the winter course of lectures. He returned to Russia by way of Vienna and showed his experiments to Ludwig, to whom he dedicated his published work, making no reference to Bernard. Sechenov became the founder of Russian experimental physiology and was also conspicuous for his championship of the education of women. In neither regard does he seem to have owed a major debt to France, since Ludwig was his acknowledged master, and there was certainly no counterpart in Bernard's laboratory of the liberality shown to women students in St. Petersburg, when Sechenov opened the doors of the Medico-Surgical Academy to them between 1860 and 1863.

It is true that young women, English, Spanish, Belgian, and Russian, as well as French, attended Bernard's lectures at the College of France, which were open to the general public. He was dismayed when "four Russian doctoresses" came to work in his laboratory. "One of them," he said, "is very young, scarcely seventeen or eighteen, but she has a heart of steel. It is amazing; they are sexless women: if all women are to be like this, I am delighted to leave the world before it becomes unbearable. It seems strange to me to see students change sex." He got on better with a young French woman whom he called "la pervenche" because her blue eyes reminded him of his favorite periwinkles. He mentioned

> . . . two young girls, delightful children of seventeen or eighteen, who sit right in front of me and take notes desperately. Their bright, intelligent faces have nevertheless a dreamy quality which is very pleasing. I feel that all the time they are taking notes on what they hear they are thinking of something else. I lament the fate of these charming children who are destined for the arid careers of school mistresses or female scientists.

The award of the Academy's prize in experimental physiology for 1859 had been an interesting one, since it had been bestowed upon Pasteur for his work on fermentation. Bernard had succeeded Magendie in the chairmanship of the committee making this award, and was therefore associated with the first formal recognition of Pasteur's work by the Academy. The general problem of fermentation had engaged Bernard's attention as early as 1851 and from 1857 to 1860 he was actively engaged upon it. His investigations were concerned primarily with the action of the digestive ferments (pancreatic juice or pepsin), but he aimed at a theory which would include an explanation of alcoholic fermentation. His general idea was that fermentation was a decomposition, and as such a strictly chemical phenomenon.

Pasteur's theory of alcoholic fermentation as essentially dependent upon the presence of a living organism was directly in opposition to Bernard's view. Bernard accepted Pasteur's experimental evidence that yeast germs were conveyed to the vines in the atmosphere, and acquiesced in the Academy's official approval of the 1860 *Memoir on Alcoholic Fermentation.* Nevertheless it is clear from the evidence of the published notebooks that he was never convinced by Pasteur's theory of "life without air," explaining alcoholic fermentation as the result of the living yeast being deprived of free oxygen which it was therefore obliged to obtain by splitting up the sugar molecule.

In the late 1850's, Bernard like everyone else, was actively concerned with the controversy over the conveyance of living organisms in the air. He was chairman of a committee of the Academy of Sciences for the award of a prize for cholera, to be paid out of a legacy left by J. Robert Bréant. This prize was never awarded during Bernard's chairmanship, although he called attention to the problem of cholera in his lectures and undertook experiments along the prescribed lines himself. He also demonstrated that growths of mold which readily appear in a solution of gelatin and sugar exposed to ordinary air are not formed if the air reaches the solution after passing through a tube heated red hot.

At the end of 1858, Felix Pouchet of Rouen made a communication to the Academy reviving the hoary theory of "spontaneous generation," and Bernard took part in the subsequent discussion. Pasteur, who felt himself the immediate object of the attack, embarked upon an elaborate series of experiments, which duplicated in principle Bernard's simple laboratory test of passing air through a red-hot tube. Pasteur's idea was to establish that the dust hovering in the air carried the spores or germs which gave rise to the swarming life visible under the microscope in a putrescent liquid. He undertook Alpine ascensions to prove that the air at great elevations and at great distances from human habitation did not carry contamination. Pouchet, on the contrary, made a journey to Sicily and found the air on Mount Etna as populous with microorganisms as the air at sea level.

All this took place during Bernard's retirement, to the

accompaniment of some fanfare in the public press. By the time he had reappeared in the Academy, Pasteur had presented a memoir on *Organized Corpuscles Existing in the Atmosphere* for the Alhumbert prize, which was set for 1862 on the question of "spontaneous generation." After conference with four of his confrères, Bernard announced the award of the prize to Pasteur for "original experiments remarkable for their precision, throwing a clear light on the conditions of production and development of a great number of inferior organisms, both animal and vegetable." In the same month Pasteur was elected to the Academy of Sciences.

Pouchet and his adherents were not silenced by the committee's decision. There were more Alpine ascensions and the debate and experiments went on. In the spring of 1863, Pasteur invited Bernard's collaboration in experiments on the putrefaction of dog's blood and urine, and in a footnote to his report remarked, "I will add, in order that you may be assured that the experiments were well conducted, that M. Claude Bernard was so obliging as to preside himself over the taking of blood." The samples of blood and urine were placed in sealed vessels and kept at 30° Centigrade from the third of March to the twentieth of April, and then exhibited to the Academy to show that no putrefaction had taken place.

The affair of "spontaneous generation" came to a climax when Pasteur gave an evening lecture at the Sorbonne in April, 1864, attended not only by the faculty, but by the Minister of Public Instruction, Duruy, by Alexandre Dumas, père, by George Sand, and by the Imperial Princess Mathilde, social *doyenne* of the intelligentsia. This audience was held in breathless attention while Pasteur exhibited his flasks (some with tortuously curved necks to sift out falling dust particles) and asked if in the face of his evidence it could still be maintained that living beings could come into the world without having been preceded by other living beings of the same species. It was the sort of thing which was always happening to Pasteur, and which he carried off so much better than Bernard could possibly have done.

Bernard may not have been able to attend the lecture. He is not mentioned in the enumeration of the more distinguished auditors, although he had been well enough to open his spring lectures at the Sorbonne and the second half of the course at the College of France. In 1863 he had taken a new flat at 14, rue Royale Saint Honoré; but no publications appeared during that year, and he had omitted the first half of his course at the College of France. His pupil Paul Bert states that a recurrence of his illness obliged him to leave Paris for Saint-Julien. However, he himself explained the omission of his winter course as being due to the long-awaited renovation of his laboratory.

The rooms now exhibited at the College of France as being in virtually the same state as when they were used by him are the laboratory, entered by a small door from the lecture amphitheater, and the small office, perhaps ten feet square, on the floor above, which he used as a private room and to receive visitors. The laboratory (which has undergone renovations) is long and narrow, dark and still damp, with glass cabinets along the walls, a large desk and sinks (not the original fixtures), and the chair used by Bernard, a simple wooden affair with curved arms, high enough to fit a tall man.

In June, 1864, Bernard resumed publication of experimental work in his friend Robin's new *Journal* with an article "On the Role of Paralyzing Reflex Actions in the Phenomena of the Secretions." This analyzed the functions of both the sensory and the two motor nerves which supply the submaxillary salivary gland. The investigation grew out of his work on this gland in connection with his final proof of the action of vasomotor and vasoconstrictor nerves in 1857. He held, as do physiologists today, that the secretion of saliva is normally the result of reflex action. A substance such as vinegar on the tongue gives rise to excitation of the sensory nerve fibers, which carry to the brain impulses which return to the gland by way of the chorda tympani, its motor nerve. The complication is that a second motor nerve, the sympathetic, has the function of constricting the blood vessels and thus diminishing the blood supply while the gland is at rest. Bernard now said that the increased blood supply accompanying stimulation of the chorda tympani and activity of the gland was due to the paralyzing influence of the chorda tympani on the sympathetic.

This was a virtual denial that the chorda tympani had the direct function of vasodilation, and, so far as his statement of theory was concerned, was a retrogression. He was in reality trying to explain what we now call "reciprocal innervation," the notion that if two opposing actions in an organ are possible, one must be suppressed in order that the other may appear. Bernard supposed this inhibitory action to lie within the innervation of the organ itself. We now know that the inhibition takes place in the central nervous system, and therefore not both motor pathways are used, but only one, in response to sensory stimulation.

A little later in the summer of 1864 Bernard published an article on derivatives of opium, based on work he had done a few months before, since he speaks of using as experimental material young sparrows "which were very plentiful in Paris in the spring." It is natural to connect his interest in this subject with the circumstance that his illness was accompanied by severe, recurrent abdominal pains. He also had an eye to his winter course, which he was planning along the same lines as those already published in *Toxic Substances.*

In September, 1864, he made his first effort in the field of popular journalism, an article on curare in the *Revue des deux mondes.* He evidently considered this subject his safest medium of approach to a lay public.

Later he thought of 1864 as the year which had introduced him for a short time to "social pleasures and their fleeting illusions" and the "political splendors" of the day. In the autumn he was invited to attend the court at Compiègne for a long week end. It was the habit of Napoleon III and the Empress Eugénie to invite literary, artistic, and academic guests along with political and social figures. A special train brought the company from Paris and carriages met the train at the station. The first evening was devoted to a formal reception. On subsequent days a variety of entertainment was provided, ranging from walks, drives, and hunting parties in the morning, through improvised lectures by visiting professors in the afternoon, to theatricals after dinner. The Emperor received some of the guests privately in his study, and the Empress held a special court over her tea table at five o'clock.

The autumn of Bernard's visit was wet and cold, and the huge guest rooms, entirely without heat, were at great distances down long corridors. On the first evening, Bernard (suitably attired in black knee breeches and silk stockings) was engaged in conversation by the Emperor. He was asked for information about his science, of which the Emperor confessed with regret that he knew nothing. Bernard discoursed steadily for two hours. The Emperor was impressed, and concluded the interview with the remark, "You are a great man of science, and I should like to have your approval."

A few days after his return to Paris, Bernard received a call from Duruy, Minister of Public Instruction. Duruy told him the Emperor wanted to know what Bernard would particularly like to have. Bernard made a general request for the improvement of equipment in the physiological laboratories of France, but Duruy pressed him to ask for a more personal favor. Bernard finally admitted that he would like a laboratory assistant for his course at the Sorbonne. Funds were provided and Bernard was able to pass on the Emperor's bounty to his pupil, Paul Bert, since 1863 his *préparateur* at the College of France.

It is often stated that Bernard and Pasteur were at Compiègne together. If so, it was not on the occasion of Bernard's first visit. The one thing which Bernard himself recorded was, characteristically, the date. Pasteur received an invitation a year later, was in turn button-holed by the Emperor on the first evening, and went on from triumph to triumph. He sent back to Paris for his microscope, invaded the royal cellars for samples of fermented wine, was received privately by the Emperor on Sunday afternoon, had the microscope carried by the Empress herself (exclaiming prettily that she was *garçon de laboratoire*) to her tea table, and delivered an informal lecture on microorganisms, which proved far more entertaining than a rival performance by Longet on the circulation of the blood. Asked to name his own reward, Pasteur obtained a six-months leave from the Normal School to continue his studies on silk worms.

Bernard was retained on the court's visiting list and is mentioned in the *Journal des Goncourts* (the famous diary published by the Goncourt brothers) as appearing in January, 1865, at a reception in the house of the Princess Mathilde, daughter of Jerome Bonaparte and cousin of Napoleon III. The Princess is the central figure of the sketch which the Goncourts left of this occasion, but Bernard impressed them too:

> Great praise is due to the Princess: chatter with stupid women and foolish men—in short, boredom—bores her; and curiously she turns that leaden color of a painting by Guercino. This evening nothing could have been funnier than the crucified expression she turned to us while we were conversing with that great and interesting scientist Claude Bernard, while she was being forced to listen to the nothings of two women.

The Princess was to have many opportunities of making up for her deprivation. In subsequent years Bernard often paid calls in her drawing room hung with crimson velvet, or dined in a room adorned with Corinthian pillars.

A year after Pasteur had given his successful evening lecture at the Sorbonne, Bernard was invited to contribute to the same series. There is no record of the occasion except the lecture itself, "A Study in the Physiology of the Heart," published afterwards in the *Revue des deux mondes*. Instead of taking up the position obvious for a physiologist that the heart is merely "a squeezing pump destined to distribute the fluid which nourishes and stimulates the functions of all the bodily organs," he undertook to justify the association of the word *heart* in literature and common speech with the emotions. He pointed out that although the characteristic movement of the heart is the earliest as well as the latest manifestation of life, and it is independent of nervous stimulus, nevertheless the nervous system exercises a negative control over its beating.

The discovery of the inhibitory action of the vagus nerve on the heart was not Bernard's, since the Weber brothers had made the observation on the frog's heart in 1845. Bernard noticed the phenomenon in 1846, when he listened to the heart sounds in a dog. When he stimulated the vagus nerve he found that they ceased, but were heard again when the stimulation was interrupted. He did not publish this result himself, but it was included in the thesis of one of his early pupils, Lefebvre, in 1848.

He did not mention these historical incidents in his evening lecture (although he insisted elsewhere on the independence of his observation from that of the Webers), but made the point that the literary use of the word *heart* has a physiological basis undreamed of by poets. A strong nerve stimulus, such as may be provoked by terror or deep emotion, will stop the heart long enough to prevent the arrival of blood in the brain, and the result will be fainting. A milder stimulus will stop the heart more briefly, imperceptibly except to the physiologist, but the function will be resumed with an increase of tempo, fluttering, or palpitation, which will send more blood to the brain, and result in a blush. Bernard therefore considered the use of such expressions as "a heart broken with grief," "a heavy heart," "a heart beating with love," "to love with the whole heart," etc., as thoroughly sound on physiological grounds. The omission of any reference to an accelerator nerve to the heart is noticeable, but accounted for by the date, since the opposite effect of the sympathetic cardiac nerves to the vagi was not demonstrated until three years later by pupils of Ludwig.

Bernard ended his address with the reflection that knowledge is an indivisible whole, and that the intuitive processes play a part in the thinking of a scientist, no less than in the interpretation of an artist:

> The artist will find more stable foundations in science, and the scientist will derive a firmer intuition from art.

Claude Bernard

Periods of crisis may doubtless arise in which science, at the same time too far in advance and as yet unperfected, disturbs and troubles the artist more than it helps him . . . ; but this is only a transitory state, and I am convinced that when physiology is far enough advanced, the poet, the philosopher, and the physiologist will all understand one another.

II

THE EXPERIMENTAL METHOD AND ITS BASIC PRINCIPLE, "SCIENTIFIC DETERMINISM" (1865)

But just what is the basis of this experimental criterion? . . . In a word, in the experimental method as in everything else, the only criterion is reason.
Introduction to the Study of Experimental Medicine.

THE CLIMAX OF BERNARD'S CAREER WAS REACHED WHEN HE presented to the Academy of Sciences, August 21, 1865, his newly published *Introduction to the Study of Experimental Medicine,* along with the seven volumes of his previously published lectures. He was then just fifty-two. The importance of the *Introduction* as an analysis of method, not only for physiology, but for the whole of biology was at once recognized. The book has remained a classic, and, more than that, a classic which is still read. It has been reprinted in France again and again, and the booksellers in the neighborhood of the School of Medicine in Paris still give it a prominent place in their windows. It is the only work of Bernard's maturity which has been translated into English.

Even a classic must be judged in its historical setting. The book announced the result of a revolution in the concluding skirmishes of which Bernard himself had taken part. The decisive battles belonged rather to the days of Magendie, who had conveyed to Bernard a vivid impression of the conflict. Bernard thought it worth while to quote Cuvier's attempt to dramatize the contrast between the rule of life and the rule of physical law by describing the surrender at the moment of death of even a young and lusty body to complete corruption. But those who still adhered to Cuvier's view that a vital force held physicochemical forces in obeyance during life could, by 1865, safely be regarded as conservatives, if not reactionaries.

Nevertheless, Bernard remarked that although a good deal of what he had to say might seem elementary to physicists and chemists, it would be differently received by many contemporary biologists, and especially physicians. There were still some of these who felt that "the study of the phenomena of living matter could not have any relation to the study of brute matter," and that life was a mysterious and supernatural influence "which acted arbitrarily in defiance of all determinism." The old doctrine kept cropping up in unexpected places. Bernard's own pupil, William Pavy, criticized the liver-washing experiment of 1855 on the ground that it had merely shown the production of sugar in the liver after death—in Pavy's opinion, not a natural, but a morbid, process. Bernard could only make the exasperated comment: "This is harking back to old vitalistic notions." In the *Introduction* he set out to destroy finally the sterile conception that there was in living things "a vital force in opposition to physicochemical forces, dominating all the phenomena of life, subjecting them to entirely separate laws, and making the organism an organized whole which the experimenter may not touch without destroying the quality of life itself."

To vindicate the experimental method Bernard asserted his conviction that its basic principle of determinism held for living as well as for inorganic material, and pointed to the impressive evidence of his own researches. For many readers the most interesting and valuable part of the *Introduction* will always be his descriptions of the successive steps of each of his principal discoveries and his consequent deduction of the way in which the mind of a scientist goes to work upon a problem. He recalled the chance observations (the clear urine of starved rabbits, crimson blood in the renal vein of the secreting kidney, the persistence of heart movements in a frog poisoned with curare) which stimulated him to "imagine" hypotheses which might explain them. He recalled also hypotheses based on a wider range of observation or upon prevailing theories, which he had formed (as in his work on the liver and glycogenesis) to provide a starting point for actual experiment, often abandoning this original hypothesis for a new one, as he followed the lead of his experimental observations.[1] The prime function of an hypothesis, however arrived at, was for him the formulation of an experimental idea. The framing of the hypothesis and the devising of experimental means to test it was the role of the intuitive or imaginative (one might almost say artistic and creative) aspect of the mind. The critical task of presiding during an experiment he gave to logical reason. When he received Paul Bert into his laboratory as *pré-*

[1] The reader may wish to refer back to the earlier chapters in which these experiments were described. For "starved rabbits" see page 51; for "secreting kidney" page 104; for persistent "heart movements" page 74; for the hypothesis out of which the work on the liver arose pages 63-64. For *proof* and *counterproof*, referred to below, compare page 65.

parateur he told him that his imagination was to be left in the cloakroom with his overcoat when he started on the actual work of an experiment, but he must not forget to put it on again when he went out.

Bernard had inherited from Magendie a dread of being biassed in his work by any systematic view or favored hypothesis. He deprecated the cluttering up of science with hypotheses which were no more than accepted theoretical explanations of phenomena insufficiently supported by experimental evidence. When the actual work of an experiment begins, the experimenter's attitude must be one in which the soundness of his provisional hypothesis and the value of his means of investigation are continually questioned. Even when an hypothesis has apparently been verified by an experiment, there must always be a reserve of doubt. Assurance may be gained through multiplication of experiments. The question, *How many animals have you used?* is still a criterion of experimental caution.

Bernard also attached great importance to what he called the *counterproof,* in which the hypothetical cause is eliminated to see if the phenomenon vanishes along with it. This was especially applicable to nerves, where a function could be demonstrated by stimulation of the nerve and abolished by cutting it.

Finally, even a verified hypothesis was granted only a provisional place in the whole body of scientific knowledge. As he expressed it:

> The theories which embody our scientific ideas as a whole are, of course, indispensable as representations of science. They should also serve as a basis for new ideas. But as these theories and ideas are by no means immutable truth, one must always be ready to abandon them, to alter them, or to replace them, as soon as they cease to

represent the truth. In a word, we must alter theory to adapt it to nature, but not nature to adapt it to theory.

The one exception to his thorough-going program of skepticism was his confidence in the principle of scientific determinism itself. As defined by Bernard, this principle means simply that under identical conditions the resulting phenomena will be identical. He virtually equated the causal interdependence of phenomena with the supremacy of reason itself:

> In fact, if the experimenter should submit his ideas to the criterion of facts, I do not admit that he should submit his reason to that test; for then he would extinguish the torch of his only inner criterion, and he would inevitably fall into the domain of the indeterminable, that is to say, the occult and the marvellous.

Bernard meant that a scientist cannot accept a "brute fact," a fact with no causal connection, no determinism, without going counter to his reason. This feeling made him return again and again in his earliest years of research to the task of tracking down apparent inconsistencies in some of Magendie's observations. Scientific determinism was the first article of Bernard's creed as a scientist.

In taking up this position Bernard was merely extending to his own science, physiology, the ideal of a rational science of nature which had been the product of seventeenth-century thought, based upon the successes of Newtonian physics. The seventeenth-century natural philosophers recognized that the very possibility of such a rational science was based upon the assumption that the natural order is a causal order. Bernard could not know that the development of thermodynamics (already under way in the middle of his own century) was to bring about a reexamination of this assumption.

A mechanical process (*e.g.*, the vibration of a pendulum in a vacuum) is a reversible process. The new and revolutionary idea that nature presents us with irreversible processes (implied in the second law of thermodynamics) confronted physics with a problem the solution to which was approached in two ways. First, the calculus of probabilities was applied to the atomistic conception of matter. Secondly, a distinction was made between atomistic and phenomenal reality, *i.e.*, between the microscopic and the macroscopic worlds. For example, the microscopic state of a gas is defined by the position and velocity of every molecule at a given moment, which our senses and measuring instruments are too crude to determine. However, a gas has aspects, such as pressure and temperature, which can be apprehended by perception and which constitute its macroscopic state. The laws which we are able to deduce regarding the macroscopic states of *irreversible processes* can only be of a statistical nature; but they are very near to being absolutely valid because of the enormous number of individual events of which these processes are composed.

At first it was considered that the possibility of statistical laws for macroscopic processes depended upon causal or necessary laws holding for microscopic processes, but the revolution was to be carried further. About 1900 even a statistical mechanics led to results not in accord with experience, and the new concept of *quantum* was introduced into physics. Close upon this followed the view that microcosmic processes (*i.e.*, processes within the atom) might not be ruled by causal laws at all, that the only kind of law in nature is statistical. This, in a summary way, is what is meant by the *indeterminism* of modern physics, which is held in some quarters to have superseded the scientific determinism of the seventeenth to the nineteenth centuries.

The plain citizen may steady himself with one or two considerations. In the first place, the new indeterminism has a practical effect only on the investigation of relations between microcosm and macrocosm. Within the limits of the macrocosm causality and determinism still hold scientific sway. Since physiology is concerned with objects of nature apprehended by perception, the determinism which Bernard advocated is still its scientific principle in practice.[2] Further, *all* physicists are deterministic in so far as the construction of their measuring instruments is concerned, and in their whole procedure up to the "first approximation."

Nonphysicists who feel that violence is being done to their reasoning powers when they are asked to forego the seventeenth-century view that the concept of probability requires the concept of causal necessity as its basis may be reassured to know that some of the older twentieth-century physicists have shared their feeling. Planck himself, whose work precipitated the *quantum* revolution, wrote in 1937 that "the only type of law fully satisfying our desire for knowledge is the strictly dynamic or (causal) type, while every statistical law is fundamentally unsat-

[2] Even physiology, however, presents situations which are most conveniently met by the methods of the *new* indeterminism (*i.e.,* not Bichat's). For example, instead of the nineteenth century belief that there are three kinds of cones in the retina and that a red, green, or blue sensation results from light striking the appropriate cone, we now entertain the possibility that there are as many as seven kinds of cones arranged in a haphazard manner. By the laws of chance one small area on the retina should have a greater proportion of one kind than another. Therefore, a ray of light impinging on one such cluster may give us a sensation of red, although the area may be by no means entirely composed of "red cones."

isfactory, for the simple reason that it has no absolute validity but admits of exceptions in certain cases." He said further that "the most important advances in the study of atomic processes are due to the attempt to look for a strictly causal and dynamic law behind every statistical law." A similar conservatism of feeling has been expressed by other physicists who believe that the indeterminism of modern physics will be reduced in importance as more is learned of the phenomena involved in atomic energy changes. One of these men has stated his position in the following terms:

> Many events are now most easily explained on the assumption that they occur spontaneously with a certain probability. Fluctuations in statistics have this same character, but are not inherently considered to be without cause. The number of atoms within a cubic centimeter of gas fluctuates with time, but if one knew the velocity, direction, and laws of collision between atoms for all particles in space, one could conceivably calculate the fluctuations to be expected. It is simply easier to handle the problem by assuming that these fluctuations are statistical.

The most widely known formalization of the dilemma of indeterminism is the Heisenberg Principle of Uncertainty, which postulates a partition separating the microcosm from the measuring apparatus presided over by an observer. This partition, in Heisenberg's view, is the seat of an indeterminacy. On one side of it the sequence of events is determined by the differential equation which is satisfied by the wave function—in which sense atomic processes are subject to the principle of causality; on the other side there is a sequence of events, determined by the laws of classical physics, which lead from the measuring apparatus to the observer. At the partitioning point the action of the instrument of observation upon the object breaks the continuity by creating an always partly uncontrollable disturbance. This amounts to an admission that determinism is unattainable by science, but does not assert that indeterminism is grounded in nature.

Recent discussion[3] of the conceptual foundations of *quantum* theory does not emphasize the noncommittal side of this solution. It asserts with confidence that the transition from the apparent caprice of the atom to the dependability of the stars in their courses can be made without change in "philosophical equipment." The *statistical* regularity observable in the microcosm is entirely compatible with individual randomness in that sphere and is also an adequate foundation for "practical lawfulness in the domain of large and heavy objects." This optimism, however, is based on the contention that "statistical regularity is the more general concept and must be regarded as primary" to mechanical lawfulness. Newtonian (classical) mechanics can be shown to be the "limiting form" of quantum mechanics, not the other way around.

According to a probably apocryphal story, Einstein said to the distinguished English mathematical physicist Dirac, "But—does God play dice?" Dirac replied, "Probably; in any case, mathematical physics is a young man's game." The nonspecialist should remember that certain principles of the Newtonian physics now obvious to schoolboys were apparently not understood by some contemporaries of Newton who were members of the Royal Society.

This excursion into the physics of the twentieth century may seem to have gone far afield, but there is no shorter way of presenting the relation of Bernard's championship of determinism in physiology and the indeterminism of atomic physics. The question whether the deterministic laws recognized by physiologists are grounded in nature

[3] Margenau, Henry: "Conceptual Foundations of the Quantum Theory," *Science,* 113: no. 2926, 95-101, January 26, 1951.

or are, philosophically, merely pragmatic (*i.e.,* it is held that these laws, in their defined sphere, are dependable) has not yet been answered to everyone's satisfaction. The chief point to grasp is that an historical relationship exists between the scientific doctrines of determinism and indeterminism, and that we are not dealing with a blunt reversal or contradiction.

Bernard himself was inclined to distrust the use of the statistical method in biological problems. He believed that "the application of mathematics to natural phenomena is the aim of all science, because phenomenal law should always be mathematically expressed," but he thought that mathematical calculations were being applied in his time to situations too crude to give significant results. He cited an investigation of nutrition based on a balance sheet of all the substances taken into a cat's body and excreted during eight days' nourishment and nineteen days' fasting, the kittens born on the seventeenth day being calculated as excreta. Another example he gave was an attempted analysis of "average European urine" based on samples from a urinal in a cosmopolitan railway station.

He was here criticizing misuse of a method rather than the method itself; but it is obvious that he failed to anticipate the extent to which the statistical method would be used to supplement the experimental method in biology. As for the way in which he would have viewed the substitution of statistical for causal law at the very foundation of science, one passage suggests that he would have felt very much as Planck continued to feel in spite of his own contribution to the new state of affairs: "I acknowledge my failure to understand why results taken from statistics are called *laws;* for in my opinion scientific law can be based only on certainty, on absolute determinism, not on probability."

His real fear was that the statistical approach might serve to prolong the reign of medical empiricism. He did not so much reject the use of statistics (although he did use his influence to discredit results obtained by that method) as regret what he considered a failure to try to get beyond them. Like Planck, he would have accepted the experimental verdict of physics, at least for the time being, in spite of an intuitive faith that only strictly causal law satisfies "our desire for knowledge."

An instance of his reliance upon instinctive belief occurs in the distinction he drew between his own doctrine of scientific determinism and the philosophic determinism, or, as he called it, the "fatalism," of the German philosopher Leibnitz. Bernard shared the widespread conviction that the human will is free, and considered the determinism of phenomena a necessary basis for human liberty. An illustration which he gave was that if the mechanism for moving your arm were not determined and fixed, you would not be free to move your arm in the direction you wished. He held, of course, that the anatomical and physicochemical "integrity" of the brain was as necessary a condition of the manifestation of free choice as its nervous connections with the muscles.

In the *Introduction* Bernard sketched in the metaphysical background which he thought necessary to support his scientific convictions. There is evidence that he tried to discover how the nature of things is accounted for by formal philosophy before he set down his own views. Among the relics at his mother's house in Saint-Julien was a small black notebook labeled "Philosophy," consisting of notes in his handwriting on two books: *History of Philosophy* translated from the German of Tenneman by Victor Cousin in 1832; and Auguste Comte's *Lectures on Positive Philosophy,* 1830. A reference to "spontaneous generation" suggests that the notebook was in use about 1864 when the *Introduction* was being revised for publication. Janet's *Le Matérialisme contemporain,* published in 1864, is the source of this reference. Janet presented his book to Bernard, who acknowledged it in one of the very few letters to his occasional correspondents which have been preserved: "Thank you for your book on Contemporary Materialism. We shall have a chat about it, especially as I find myself at the moment trespassing on your philosophical domain. . . . (April 27, 1864)."

The closing sections of the *Introduction* and an essay which Bernard published in 1865 on *Progress in the Physiological Sciences* virtually reproduce each other, except for shorter paragraphing in the essay, apparently with the limitations of the casual reader in mind. Here Bernard states his opinion of the contribution of philosophy to human knowledge. A comparison with the black notebook shows that reflection or courtesy made him more restrained in published opinions than in private jottings. In the notebook he remarks: "The philosopher who is not a scientist is sterile and presumptuous" and "philosophers are mere intellectual gymnasts." He called Francis Bacon, from whom he often borrowed turns of expression for his published works, a mere "trumpet and town crier" and no experimenter. In the *Introduction* he admits that he liked the philosophers he knew. He goes on:

> From the scientific point of view, philosophy represents the eternal aspiration of the human reason toward knowledge of the unknown. That is why philosophers always carry on their activities on controversial ground and in lofty regions, the upper boundaries of science. In this way they impart to scientific thought a movement which

> enlivens and ennobles it; they develop and strengthen the mind by general intellectual gymnastics.

This is suaver than calling a philosopher an intellectual gymnast, but still directs attention to what Bernard considered the limitations of philosophy.

He would not admit that his own position was derived from what he called "systems," fetters depriving a scientist of intellectual freedom. In a letter he wrote:

> In my view, it is not in the extreme positions called materialism or spiritualism that the solution is to be found. Neither is it in eclecticism, which is only a mosaic of ideas, nor in pantheism which confounds everything in the identity of the nonidentical, as Hegel said.

As for positivism, under which historians of philosophy incline to classify him, he said in the *Introduction* that it was as much a system as the philosophical systems which it repudiated. He does not mention Auguste Comte in his published works, but the *Introduction* has several disparaging references to the "philosophical school which prides itself on being founded on science." Of Emile Littré he wrote in a letter of 1874:

> Thank you for your article on Littré; I shall return it to you tomorrow. I find you too enthusiastic over the narrow and rigid conceptions adorned by the name of positivism.

Nevertheless Bernard's sketch of the evolution of medicine through successive stages in his notes for his *Principles of Experimental Medicine* is reminiscent of Comte's evolutionary law and his agnosticism may perhaps be distinguished only verbally from the positivist view of the same problem. He made a distinction between primary causes, which he deemed inaccessible to scientific investigation, and secondary causes, the elucidation of which was the object of scientific experimentation. How far back in his thinking this division of causes went is shown in his first series of lectures as professor at the College of France in 1855 when he said: "We shall not need to investigate *why* this primitive cell produces such a being rather than another. . . . These questions of first or final causes do not in my opinion belong to the domain of science."

Since the view appears so early, before Bernard's consciously reflective period, it may have been absorbed from the temper of the times. At the time of the *Introduction* he still believed there was no way of transcending it. In the essay published in the same year in the *Revue des deux mondes* he said: "In vital and physical phenomena alike a complete knowledge of the conditions of their existence, *i.e.*, of their secondary causation, tells us nothing of their ultimate nature."

There are indications in the jotted reflections of his later years, apparently assembled with a view to a second edition of the *Introduction,* and published under the title *Pensées* (1937), that he became critical of too rigid a hierarchy of secondary causes and of the possibility of isolating the immediate cause. He wrote without giving the reflection a definite date:

> I admit an *initial* cause of the world, but I do not recognize a *final* cause. I am ignorant of the final cause because I am ignorant of the initial cause. I abstain in the case of the one as of the other; for I am reduced in both cases to invent, to imagine, without being able to prove anything.
>
> I no longer recognize intermediary or immediate causes. There is everywhere only transformation of phenomena from one form to another, according to a neces-

> sary equilibrium and harmony, at the same time conserving a sort of independence or autonomy.
>
> The result is that autonomous phenomena are harmonized without being bound in logical relations of cause to effect. Thus, the *area vasculosa* of the egg develops even when the embryo is lacking.

The direction of his thought becomes clearer in the light of his illustrations: while it is not certain that the sun will rise tomorrow, it is certain that it will rise if the conditions of its rising are not altered; two and two make four, provided that the brain has a certain construction. He says that only relationships are real, that an effort must be made to escape from the absolute of the century just past into the relativity of the new century. In the living cell everything depends upon everything else.

Up to this point there is no distinction to be made between the position of the sciences dealing with organic and inorganic material. A little reflection will suggest the difficulties (of which Bernard was completely aware) of applying to biological material, except in rather an ideal way, his definition of determinism, that constant conditions produce constant results. He was very conscious of the *individuality* (his own word) of the determinism of living beings. One section of the *Introduction* dealt with "the diversity of mammals submitted to experimentation." He was ready to admit that one animal can never be fully compared to another, and that the same animal cannot be compared to itself at various times of examination. However, instead of concluding that this made animals ineligible for experimentation, he saw that it was rather a reason which made any other approach than the experimental one impossible for living material, although the problems of that experimentation would be of an especially challenging kind. It is necessary to consider what an experiment really implies.

Bernard defined an experiment as an induced or provoked observation. He thought that astronomy was a good example of an observational science, since the stars are set in unalterable courses. In the physical, chemical, and, in his view, the biological sciences (including physiology), we have the advantage of being able in some degree to manipulate the material. It is problematic whether identical conditions can ever be realized a second time in an organism which is in a constant process of development and of changing relationships among its parts. But the very nature of an experiment permits the limitation and simplification of causal situations and the isolation of moments in the history of the organism. Since these things are done deliberately, they can be taken account of. The very artificiality of the experimental situation can be turned to advantage.

The characteristic of living beings, especially warm-blooded animals, which particularly interested Bernard was their possession of an isolating and protective "internal environment," which intervened between organic elements of the body and the external environment. He noted in the *Introduction* that the self-regulatory character of the fluid medium in which the elements of the organism exist makes control for the physiological experimenter more difficult and complicated than for the physicist dealing with temperature and pressure which he can regulate with a thermometer and a barometer. At the time of the *Introduction* he was less interested than he subsequently became in the unity of the organism and in problems of integration other than those implied by the organism's fluid internal environment. Nevertheless, he was fully alive to all aspects of the special nature of the subject matter of physiology. He could say: "I should agree with the vitalists if they would simply recognize that living beings exhibit phenomena peculiar to themselves and unknown in inorganic nature."

At the end of the section of the *Introduction* in which he discussed considerations "special to living beings," Bernard used an expression crystallizing his view that recognition of the directive forces of life was necessary, especially for the problems of generation, development, and nutrition of the organism. Here he used the phrase "the directive *idea* of this vital evolution." It is worth noting that "the directive idea" (*l'idée directrice*) is not found in the very complete index of Bernard's writings published by his pupils after his death. The term stood for a conception upon which the prevailing materialism and positivism of the 1870's, consciously or unconsciously, was not likely to place emphasis. Bernard's own explanation of what he meant by the directive idea was this:

> When a chicken develops in an egg, it is not the formation of the animal body, considered as a grouping of chemical elements, which essentially characterizes the vital force. This grouping occurs only in pursuance of the laws which preside over the physicochemical properties of matter; but what belongs essentially to the domain of life and not to chemistry, or physics, or anything else, is the directive *idea* of this vital evolution. In every living germ there is a creative idea which is developed and revealed by organization. During its whole existence, the living being remains under the influence of this same creative vital force, and death comes when it can no longer be realized. Here as everywhere everything depends upon the idea which alone creates and directs; the means of physicochemical manifestation are common to all the phenomena of nature and lie pell-mell, like the letters of the alphabet in a box, where a directing influ-

ence seeks them out to express the most varied thoughts or mechanisms.

There has been much debate as to whether the *directive idea* represents a backsliding into the vitalism which Bernard had so vigorously attacked. To him, adherence to the principle of determinism made all the difference. In the passage immediately following the one quoted he returns, as if in self-justification, to the position that it is only through understanding of the physicochemical conditions of primal development that the physiologist or physician can take action. A physics and chemistry "carried out in the special field of life" is therefore the proper basis of their activities.

This is not to say that there was vacillation on Bernard's part between two positions. Rather, the matter had two aspects of equal importance to him. The philosopher Bergson has said that Bernard was less concerned to provide a definition of *life* than of *the science of life*. Bernard was obliged first to show that a science of life was possible. He accomplished this by proving that vital phenomena were subjected to a determinism as dependable as that which prevailed in the physical sciences. He could then go on to exhibit the characteristics of the subject matter of his science which were unique. When he spoke of the directive or creative *idea* of the vital organism, he had in mind the unique way in which the organism is *intelligible* to the scientist, in terms of its wholeness and historical continuity. He would never have undertaken to answer the questions whether this idea existed in the mind of God, or whether the simplest organic unit is in some sense *knowing;* he would have been content, granting that an idea must have its existence in some mind, to have the *directive idea of vital evolution* exist as a "principle of interpretation" (Bergson's phrase) in the mind of the physiologist.

In December, 1865, six months after the *Introduction* appeared, Bernard sketched on a dozen manuscript sheets the plan of the work it was meant to introduce: *Principles of Experimental Medicine.* He wished to emphasize "the vital point of view" in contrast to the Germans who, he thought, "paid too much attention to the purely physical side of nervous and muscular action." He believed that one of the best things he had done was "to have insisted on the *physiological* conditions of experiments," so often neglected before him. He therefore planned "to regularize operative procedure in the experimental analysis of the living body."

His other chief object was to establish the true relationship between experimental physiology and scientific medicine. He was uncomfortably aware of the contemporary opposition to giving physiology its proper status, which had taken the form against him personally of a delay of sixteen years in his election to the Academy of Medicine. He had applied in 1845, but was admitted only in 1861. He had been accused of "substituting the laboratory for the hospital," but he always advised aspirants to a career in physiology to "go through the hospitals first." In the light of what Bernard said himself, Renan's remarks in his Academic eulogy that Bernard "was as little a physician as possible" and "a skeptic before the altar which he served" seem a little shallow. It is true that Bernard did not practice medicine, but he was profoundly interested in the future of medicine as a science. In his projected book he planned to show that the analytical studies of experimental medicine were theoretically as well as practically subsequent to the observational medicine of the hospital by illustrating the evolutionary progress of medicine through its prescientific, its empirical, its observational, and its experimental stages.

He embarked upon a preliminary historical review, but almost at once the first of what he afterwards called "a thousand obstacles" turned him aside from the task. The notebook devoted to accumulating material for it was finally published by Delhoume only in 1947.

12

SECOND ILLNESS AND RETURN FROM RETIREMENT (1865–1869)

Vexations and honors have been heaped upon me simultaneously, and some gleams of hope have appeared like a vivifying ray of sunlight in a transient patch of clear sky between two dark clouds; but little by little, as happens when a storm subsides, the heavens take on the misty and monotonous hue of the life which henceforth awaits me. Letter to Mme. Raffalovich, 1869.

IN AUGUST, 1865, JUST BEFORE THE PRESENTATION OF THE *Introduction* to the Academy of Sciences, Bernard was appointed a member of a deputation to represent that body at the unveiling of a statue to the astronomer François Arago, in the village of Estagel, near Perpignan, in the south of France. Among his traveling companions were M. Barral, the publisher of Arago's works and proprietor of a bookshop in the rue Jacob, and his son George Barral. The latter was greatly struck by Bernard's appearance, his tall figure and the "sculptural lines" of his head. Bernard, he thought, looked like "a modern saint in lay dress, a sort of Vincent de Paul of science." Bernard and the Barrals were fellow guests of one of the local officials, and the foundations of a long friendship were laid.

On his return to Paris, Bernard succumbed once more to his chronic abdominal trouble and Dr. Rayer and Dr. Davaine resumed their attendance. The symptoms were so severe that they thought Bernard might have been infected by the cholera, then epidemic in Paris. He was unable to give his winter course, and for a time it was feared he would not recover. Toward the end of April, 1866, he left his family in a new flat at 24 rue de Luxembourg, and went down to Saint-Julien, accompanied by Dr. Davaine.

Here he took over his own case, living simply and carefully, making a daily study of his symptoms. It was remembered in Saint-Julien afterward that all the garden spinach went to him, and the grapes from the trellis, certain clusters being wrapped up so that they would ripen slowly. Every day he ordered a loaf of rye bread. Dr. Jousset described his disease as a chronic enteritis with symptoms affecting the pancreas and the liver. Sir Michael Foster thought that in the late nineties it would have been recognized as chronic appendicitis, and the youthful illness of 1833 was possibly of this sort. The more contemporary suggestion of a peptic ulcer, scarcely less often the occupational ailment of the experimental physiologist than of the business executive, has to recommend it Bernard's association of the incidence of attacks with nervous tension.

He was strong enough to spend a good deal of time sitting on the "bench of Sisyphus" in the shade of his six yew trees, looking at the view and pondering his problems. At times he was so disheartened at again being cut off from the scientific world that the melancholy of his letters to Paris alarmed his friends. The Emperor telegraphed for news of his health, and his vinegrower rose to the occasion by carrying the reply to the sovereign all the way to the telegraph office in Villefranche.

A little later, early in November, 1866, when it was learned that the graver symptoms had been overcome, Pasteur had the idea of improving the convalescent's morale by publishing in *Le Moniteur universel,* the official journal of the Second Empire, an article on Bernard's contributions to science. Having read afresh Bernard's principal memoirs, the published lectures, and the *Introduction,* he said he could not resist putting into words the admiration he felt for the genius expressed in these works. He singled out for detailed comment the discovery of the glycogenic function of the liver, and showed how the stages of its development corresponded with Bernard's analysis of the experimental method in the *Introduction.* He spoke also of the increasing possibility of a really scientific medicine opened up by physiological discovery. He quoted the reply of the chemist Dumas when asked by Duruy for his opinion of "this great physiologist." Dumas had said: "Bernard is not a great physiologist; he is physiology itself." Pasteur added:

> I have spoken of the scientist; I would like to make known the man whom I have met from day to day, the colleague who has been able to inspire so many firm friendships, for when I look for Bernard's weak side, I do not find one. The distinction of his bearing, the noble beauty of his countenance, stamped with a great gentleness, an amiable kindness, are immediately charming; he has no pedantry, no scholar's eccentricity, an old-fashioned directness, a natural manner in conversation, as far as possible removed from affectation, but well nourished with ideas at once sensible and profound.

In a letter sent a few days later to Henri Saint-Claire Deville, in acknowledgment of a message of congratulation on the improvement of his health signed by half a dozen of his friends, Bernard wrote, "This article paralyzed the vasomotor nerves of my sympathetic system and caused me to blush up to my eyes." To Pasteur himself he wrote:

> . . . It is a very precious encouragement to be praised by a man such as you. . . . The admiration which you profess for me is indeed reciprocated; and we must have been born to understand each other, for true science inspires us both with the same passion and the same sentiments.
>
> Forgive me for not having answered your first letter: but I really was not equal to writing the notice you wanted. I felt deeply for you in your family sorrow. I too have passed through this trial and I can understand how someone as sensitive and tender-hearted as yourself must have suffered.
>
> I intend to return to Paris soon and give as much of my course this winter as I can. As you say in your article, the acute symptoms seem to have disappeared, but I still need to be very careful; the least fatigue, the least departure from my regimen puts me back again. . . .

The allusion in "family sorrow" was to the death of Pasteur's twelve-year-old daughter from typhoid fever, after the loss of two other daughters, one in 1859, the other in 1865, and to Bernard's own loss of two infant sons.

As it turned out, he was not able to return to Paris during the winter of 1866-1867. The only event of 1866 was the publication of the lectures delivered two years before at the Sorbonne under the title *Properties of Living Tissues.* Bernard was occupied during his semi-invalidism with a task laid on him by the Minister of Public Instruction.

Napoleon III was planning a French exhibition to rival Prince Albert's in Victorian England during 1862. To call attention to the intellectual as well as the material accomplishments of France, he instructed Duruy to invite a number of scholars to prepare reports on the progress of letters and sciences for publication by the Imperial press. Bernard was asked to present the report on general physiology. He remarked, in introducing the notes on his sources, that the "difficult conditions" under which it was prepared had prevented him from making it a "work of erudition."

The guiding plan of the series was to give a résumé of French achievement during the past quarter century. Bernard added a backward glance at Lavoisier and Laplace, whom he regarded as the pioneers of physiology in France because their work on respiration and animal heat had established that the same physical and chemical laws hold for animate as for inanimate bodies. Bichat had opposed this principle, but his anatomical studies of the tissues nevertheless gave general physiology its proper point of departure. The renaissance (Bernard's own expression) of physiology at the beginning of the nineteenth century was completed when Magendie by precept and example made the science experimental.

Bernard gave Magendie full credit for the discovery of the difference in function between the dorsal and ventral roots of the spinal nerves. Eleven years before he had been content to say that Magendie had been the first to provide experimental proof of a distinction already understood by Charles Bell. At some time between 1856 and 1867 he had consulted Bell's 1811 pamphlet and revised his opinion of Bell's grasp of the matter. In the *Rapport sur les progrés et la marche de la physiologie générale en France* (*Report on the Progress and Achievements of General Physiology in France*) Bernard recorded his considered judgment that the honor of the discovery of the functions of the spinal nerve roots belonged to Magendie and to

France, and he added that "whoever will read the successive memoirs of Charles Bell and Magendie, going back to the time of their first publication and the original texts," will concur.

He was obliged to rely rather heavily on his own researches to make up the French contribution, but referred to the work of about forty scientists, giving special commendation to Brown-Séquard and Pasteur. His effort to be fair to Longet was obvious, but he made it clear that Longet had been unfair to Magendie. A curious omission was that of Flourens, whose work on the control of coordination by the cerebellum and on other aspects of the nervous system had been outstanding.

He included contemporary repetition of some of Geoffroy Saint-Hilaire's experiments and touched on fundamental ideas which always appear in attempts to account for the evolution of species, *e.g.,* variation in types under changing external influences. He also set the seal of his approval on the doctrine of the transmission of acquired characters, although he made no reference to *transformisme,* as evolution was called in France, nor did he discuss the theories of Darwin and Lamarck. He was inclined to be lukewarm toward developments in science which did not lead to immediate experimental verification.

He introduced the theme of the unique qualities of living beings in the discussion of his concept of the internal environment, and in the section on the development of organic tissues. This makes the *Report,* and the essay summarizing its general argument published under the title *The Problem of General Physiology,* important source material, supplementing the *Introduction,* for Bernard's general philosophical position.

What was stressed in the *Report* was the physiologist's need of special laboratory facilities adapted to the special nature of his subject matter. At the same time Bernard avoided giving any foothold to the reactionary view that the phenomena of life were less amenable to determinism than the phenomena of physical substances. He even suggested the possibility of producing new organized species through "modification of the nutritive and evolutive interior environment," but added that this would not mean more than the realization of "organic forms which exist potentially in the laws of organogenesis, but which nature itself has not yet realized," and that it would be comparable to the creation of a new mineral compound.

Early in July, 1867, Bernard's mother died at her home in Saint-Julien and a week or two later Bernard returned to Paris with the manuscript of the *Report.* It was another year and a half before he resumed his lectures, but he gradually took on a number of social and scientific engagements.

During 1867 two of his close friends, Pelouze and Rayer, died. Two months after the death of Rayer (who had been president of the Society of Biology since its foundation), Bernard was elected to the life presidency of this society, but did not assume his duties until the following March. He was also advanced to the rank of Commander in the Legion of Honor. On the death of Flourens he was urged to apply for his vacated seat in the French Academy, by virtue of the literary success of his *Introduction to the Study of Experimental Medicine.* He set about making the necessary calls upon persons of influence and was elected in May, 1868, but did not take his seat formally until a year later.

He resumed his chairmanship of the committee which awarded the Academy of Sciences' prize in experimental physiology. Among the works considered for the prize of 1867 was E. Cyon's on the innervation of the heart. He and his brother had been carrying on their researches partly in Berlin in the laboratory of Du Bois-Reymond, and partly at Leipzig, with the collaboration of Ludwig.

Bernard took a special interest in Cyon's work which dealt with the conveyance of sensory impulses from the heart and the mechanism by which the heart can be relieved of too great a load. He himself had observed the sensitivity of the inner walls of the heart on inserting thermometers into that organ. He also considered the mechanism described by Cyon as an example of the same sort of "paralyzing reflex" which he had postulated, rather unfortunately, for the vasodilator effect of stimulation of the chorda tympani. In the very next year the Cyon brothers completed their account of the innervation of the heart, showing that the sympathetic cardiac nerves had an effect opposite to that of the vagi, namely, an accelerating one. The work is a symptomatic instance of how the current of successful physiological investigation was beginning to set toward Germany and the pupils of Ludwig.

Early in 1868 Bernard was invited to a conference of scientists and the Imperial administration on the condition of research laboratories in France. This arose from the agitation of Pasteur who, seeking funds for a new laboratory of physiological chemistry, published in the *Revue des cours scientifiques* an article describing some of the existing installations: his own corner under a stairway on the mezzanine at the Normal School, the damp, dark laboratory of chemistry, a yard below street level, at the Sorbonne, and the experimental quarters, half cellar, half grave, of Bernard at the College of France. He attributed Bernard's long illness to conditions in his laboratory, and quoted Bernard's reference to French laboratories as the "tombs of scientists."

The Emperor summoned Pasteur, Bernard, Saint-Claire Deville, and Milne-Edwards as representatives of science, and Rouher, Vaillant, and Duruy for the government, inviting suggestions from each. The proposal finally acted upon for Bernard came from Pasteur, who pointed out the possibility of converting space available at the Museum of Natural History into a laboratory. Following a decree approved in August, Bernard resigned his chair at the Sorbonne in favor of Paul Bert, and transferred his course in General Physiology to the Museum of Natural History.

Pasteur had strengthened his case with the Emperor by his account of the research facilities provided in Germany. Bernard was fascinated by what he learned of these establishments, although his curiosity never drove him to the point of visiting them. He was especially interested in the laboratory at Amsterdam of his pupil, W. Kühne, and in that of Ludwig at Leipzig. He was struck with the convenience of a laboratory which included living quarters for the professor and he admired Ludwig's plan of internal organization, which separated, and at the same time combined, the pursuits of animal experimentation, physiological chemistry, and histology. He planned to copy this arrangement at the Museum, but never succeeded in including a histological section. He did, however, persuade the administration to establish an histological laboratory at the College of France seven years later, and appoint his pupil, L. Ranvier, to the newly created post.

Bernard's health continued precarious, although he suffered no actual breakdown. He had made a rule since 1865 against accepting invitations to dinner, because he was obliged to eat sparingly or not at all in the evening, but he put in an appearance now and then on great occasions. He is mentioned by the Goncourts among the guests of Princess Mathilde in April, 1868. He and the poet Gautier are described as looking like ghosts, Bernard in particular wearing "the mask of a man brought back from the tomb."

He devoted his next holiday to the preparation of his reception speech in the Academy. Three or four manuscript drafts of the address, mingled in confusion, were eventually found in the attic of his house at Saint-Julien. In the printer's proof which also survives, Bernard's interlinear corrections and rearrangements show that he was still trying to improve it at this late stage. He came back to Paris toward the end of the year, for in December he was again at the Princess Mathilde's, this time looking like a "specter of science."

In January, 1869, he resumed his lectures at the College of France. He explained to the first class how he had reconciled himself to enforced leisure for so long:

> We are about to resume our studies in experimental medicine which have been interrupted very much against my will for three years. I have reason to regret this interruption deeply; for this lacuna in my scientific life is precious time forever lost. Unhappily for me I had all this time for reflection, but I was able to use the leisure which my illness left me to organize my ideas and form projects for study which will not be without value in the course we are about to resume. I have only one desire, that is, that my health, the present state of which will oblige me sometimes to appeal to your indulgence, may gradually mend and allow me still to serve that science to which I have devoted my entire life.

He spoke of plans for his new laboratory, and announced that the course would be devoted that year to "experimental technique as applied to physiology and experimental medicine." This implied that much time would be devoted to the details of experiments and operations; but a good deal of attention was also given to exposition of his view of the special nature of living experimental material in a form reminiscent of the *Introduction* and the *Report.*

At one of the later lectures of this course Bernard had a new auditor, who introduced herself to him as an admirer of his *Introduction.* She was Mme. Hermann Raffalovich, wife of a Russian Jewish financier living in Paris. Worried about her health, she asked Bernard's advice. He arranged for a consultation, pointing out that he did not ordinarily practice, and eventually recommended that she put herself in the care of the eminent surgeon Richet. This acquaintance, beginning with Mme. Raffalovich's interest in Bernard as the champion of scientific medicine, soon ripened into their lasting friendship.

Mme. Raffalovich had cosmopolitan charm and culture. Born in Odessa, where she married at sixteen, she could still in 1869 be described by Bernard as "a young and pretty woman" whose "superiority of mind" he admired. She was a fine linguist, contributed "unpaid" articles on French life and literature to the St. Petersburg *Journal,* and enjoyed philosophical discussion. Bernard felt that her gifts supplemented his own, for he was comfortable neither with foreign tongues nor systematic philosophy. He had confidence in her ability not only to translate but to abstract scientific books and papers and was soon making use of her in this way to an astonishing extent. He valued her as a listener on whom his original philosophical views could be tried out, although he sometimes brushed her criticisms aside in a magisterial manner. He was greatly attracted by her family circle, to which she was devoted, her husband, her parents, her three children (a grown son, Arthur, a younger daughter, Sophie, and the youngest, André, called playfully Monsieur Bébé).

Since she had already read the *Introduction,* Bernard

presented her with his *Report,* the appended notes to which he thought better presented his philosophical position. She wrote him a criticism, apparently not too adverse, and he began to dine at her house and call on Sunday afternoons. In time he set aside Thursday from five to seven for a regular weekday call and Sophie, who remembered Bernard with affection, later remarked that she liked to stay to listen during these visits, although usually she fled when callers were announced. On one occasion Bernard arrived with a present of chicks which had broken out of their shells the day before at the laboratory.

The announcement or cancellation of visits resulted in many notes which Bernard despatched in place of the modern telephone call. Mme. Raffalovich preserved these and some longer letters written during the holidays at Saint-Julien over a period of nine years and after Bernard's death presented the collection (about five hundred letters) to the Library of the Institute, where it may still be consulted in manuscript.[1] Bernard also kept Mme. Raffalovich's letters, but she gave instructions at his death that they were to be destroyed as she thought them of no value. A debt of gratitude is owing to her for her disposition of Bernard's letters, for these provide an almost day-to-day account of his interests and activities for the last decade of his life. Their frequency attests the importance of this friendship to him, for he was disinclined to letter writing. One of the few surviving letters outside the Raffalovich collection includes an apology: "I am an 'epistolophobe' by nature and have on my conscience hundreds, perhaps I should say thousands, of letters I have never answered."

---

[1] A selection from Bernard's letters to Mme. Raffalovich, who did not exercise her right to forbid publication when she made her bequest, has been edited by Justin Godart under the title *Lettres Beaujolaises* (Villefranche-en-Beaujolais. Éditions du Cuvier, 1950).

During 1869 Bernard's domestic affairs came to a sudden crisis. It is not known on just what day Mme. Bernard and her two daughters left the apartment in the rue du Luxembourg, or what were the events which provoked her decision. It seems unlikely that the old quarrel over vivisection could have been acute at this time, since Bernard had been withdrawn from his laboratory for a number of years. It has been alleged that Mme. Bernard was very conscious of having contributed her dowry to the household and was dissatisfied with the way in which it had been used. She apparently did not accompany her husband on his visits to Saint-Julien after 1865. Beginning with the first of May, 1866, Bernard's stipend from the Sorbonne, some six hundred francs a month, was paid directly to Mme. Bernard as housekeeping money. Bernard also paid the rent of the flat and, on at least one recorded occasion, the wages of a maid "who was leaving." He controlled the income from the College of France and from the vintage at Saint-Julien. Early in 1869 he wrote to the Mother Superior of the Maison du Sacré-Coeur withdrawing a request for rooms for his wife and daughters, since Mme. Bernard had declined them on learning that she would be unable to take her two dogs with her.

Although the Bernards began to live apart in 1869, a formal decree of separation was obtained only in April, 1870, "without publicity, thanks to the political influence which Bernard had at his disposal at this time," according to Jousset. At the time of the decree Bernard's address was given as the rue Luxembourg and Mme. Bernard's as the rue Cherchemidi. Eventually she and her two daughters withdrew to Bezons (Seine-et-Oise). There is no record of a monetary settlement, but any borrowings from the dowry would necessarily have been reimbursed at this time. In the division of the household goods Bernard asked for half the silver and linen, an ivory Christ, a carved-oak stoup, the pictures of his children, some of their books, especially one which had been a gift of the Empress Eugénie, and "the various little things which belonged to my last child."

The request for the religious objects is a little unexpected and the one for the Empress's book surely a little selfish. The former may be related to the fact that, while Bernard ignored religious observances in Paris, he attended services in the village church at Saint-Julien and was on good terms with the parish priest. He seems to have liked to remember his children when they were very young, and his special feeling for his youngest son is shown in the request for the playthings. His daughters were now young women of twenty-two and nineteen, completely under their mother's influence and in agreement with her views. Neither of them ever married.

Although Bernard was reticent about his misfortunes, he conveyed the impression that he suffered from having missed domestic happiness. He wrote cryptically to Mme. Raffalovich: "The year 1869 will have been for me a period of disquieting and painful change in which the most diverse events have occurred." In the Academy speech, upon which he had been working during his country holiday, he had written that Flourens "found by his fireside the calm and repose so necessary for a hard-working scientist." He went on: "His wife, devoted, well fitted to understand and appreciate him, identified herself with his intellectual life, to which she gave greater scope by shielding him from the very cares of existence."

Bernard had come to feel that community of interests was important for the success of a marriage. He knew also that deep affection could bridge a gulf, for he never lost sympathy with his peasant mother, who was a little dazzled by the success of her son but was able to share it during his annual visits to Saint-Julien. His arrival was her great occasion, and she saw that he was well taken care of under her roof. She was active all her life, and kept control of her small property and the vintage from it. There was a story at Saint-Julien (where Mme. Claude Bernard was generally regarded as a little insane) that when Mme. Pierre Bernard heard of the impending separation of her son and daughter-in-law she collapsed under a stroke and died within a few hours. This may be no more than country gossip. Jeanne Bernard, who had been twenty-five when her son was born, died July 6, 1867, aged seventy-eight. In 1871, on the occasion of the death of Charles Robin's mother, Bernard wrote: "I share with you the unhappiness which comes to you in the death of your mother. Three years ago I had the grief of losing mine, and I know by experience that it is one of the greatest sorrows in life."

On May 27, 1869, Bernard assumed his seat in the French Academy and delivered the reception speech which he had so carefully prepared. An Academician's first appearance among his *confrères* has been compared to a first night at the theater. There is a rush for tickets among the wives, daughters, sisters, widows, cousins, and aunts of members, and great competition for advantageous places. The candidate, arrayed in a ceremonial costume with lavish green embroideries, a cocked hat, gloves, and a sword on the left hip, presents himself at a desk where the Director of the Academy is seated between the permanent Secretary and the Chancellor. The candidate makes his address, to which the Secretary replies. According to the Goncourts, the reason for the long delay between Bernard's election and his reception (a year) was that the Secretary Guillaume Patin, a classical scholar, "forgets every day at the foot of the stairs the physiology which the physiologist has taught him in his office."

It is a little difficult to understand why the composition of Bernard's reception speech had given him so much trouble, since it is simple and direct, adorned by only one or two modest similes. This very simplicity may have disappointed an audience with perhaps some taste for rhetoric, for the address was rather coldly received. There may also have been a feeling that the speech did not quite do justice to Flourens. Bernard's account of Flourens' scientific work was a little impersonal. He chose not to deal with Flourens' experimentation in detail but to survey the relationships of the various nerve centers which the work had elucidated.[2] It should be remembered that in his eulogy of Magendie before the Academy of Sciences, Flourens had taken the side of Bell in the controversy over priority in the discovery of the functions of the spinal nerve roots. Bernard may have had difficulty in doing justice to a man who had certainly done less than justice to Magendie.

In acknowledgment that his election was a tribute to the *Introduction,* Bernard referred to certain familiar articles of the creed expressed in that work, for example, that the experimental method is not concerned with the primary cause of phenomena, which escapes its processes of investigation. The recurrent theme of the speech is the indivisibility of knowledge and of the intuitive and rational aspects of the intelligence, a theme developed before in his Sorbonne lecture on the *Physiology of the Heart.* It was central to his thought and when he spoke of it, "his language," in the words of the best modern French critic of his style, Jean Rostand, "suddenly, without losing

[2] It is curious that in Bernard's essay of 1872 on the *Functions of the Brain,* illustrated by a picture of Flourens' pigeon with the cerebral lobes removed, there should be no mention of Flourens in the text.

its magnificent sobriety, becomes charged with a deep and vibrating emotion":

> We need the unknown to arouse and torment us, and it is the unknown which constantly spurs our aspirations in the search for new truths of which our *feeling* has a deep intuition, but of which our *reason,* by means of experiment, seeks to find the scientific formula.

Rostand is aware of the imperfections which disturb a reader beginning the *Introduction* with a full sense of its reputation. He says:

> To be sure, Claude Bernard turns out to be no purist; his style, often heavy and loose, abounds in repetition of words and even of ideas. But the consistent elevation of his views, the proud distinction of the thought, the natural nobility and firm virility of expression, the tone of conviction and seriousness which animates the least phrase, makes this book a master work of our literature. We meet not only a scientist but a man, and a man who, having spent his life in the dramatic pursuit of truth, makes us share the anxieties of research and the pure joy of discovery, the liveliest which the human spirit can feel. Claude Bernard has put the whole of himself there, his burning desire for knowledge, his contagious passion for truth, his fine austerity, his distrust for mere words and dogmatic opinion, his lucid enthusiasm for the experimental method. When he speaks of the grandeur of science, of the inflexibility of determinism, of man's power over nature, the accents he finds are unforgettable.

Bernard himself, struggling with an unreceptive audience, which perhaps had been warned that public speaking was not his strong point, made only one concession to the fact that literary criticism was one of the prime functions of the Academy. In appreciation of Flourens' style, expressing at the same time his own standards, he said: "The eloquence of a scientist is clarity; scientific truth is always more luminous when its beauty is unadorned than when it is tricked out in the embellishments with which our imagination would seek to clothe it."

At the conclusion of the ceremony Bernard had become one of the forty Immortals of France, entrusted with guardianship over the purity of the French language as preserved by the Academy's revisions of its dictionary. He was often thereafter to complain half jestingly to Mme. Raffalovich of the tedious sessions devoted to this task. His Academy seat was numbered twenty-four. His Academician's sword with the Imperial eagle on its hilt he laid away for safekeeping in a drawer at Saint-Julien.

The French Academy is the senior of the five Academies comprising the Institute, the other four being Fine Arts, Inscriptions, Moral and Political Sciences, and Physical and Mathematical Sciences. Bernard had been a member of the last-named since 1854. During 1868 he had declined the secretaryship on grounds of health but had accepted the vice-presidency. In 1869 he was chosen president for that year, and in that capacity addressed the joint session of the five Academies on August 14. It was customary for the president of one of the Academies to open the session with an address on the history and purposes of the Institute. Bernard spoke, naturally enough, on the increasing importance of the sciences in modern civilization.

Earlier in the year, May 6, 1869, an Imperial decree had made him Senator. The duties of the Senate of the Second Empire, as defined by the Emperor, were to watch over the general welfare of France, propose useful reforms, and appear at public functions "in full dress with blue trousers." In fact it merely lent itself to the purposes of a thoroughly autocratic administration, and Bernard in becoming Senator was virtually accepting the position of pensioner of the Imperial government. His yearly income was augmented by the sum of 60,000 francs, of which he actually received five quarterly payments, as is witnessed by a card bearing five stamps, which he did not destroy when the Second Empire perished.

There is no suggestion that Bernard was in any way critical of the government of Napoleon III. He mentioned in his Academy reception speech "the striking marks of interest" bestowed upon his science "by sovereigns." He was exemplary in attendance and in voting from the day when he took his seat in August, 1869, until the Senate was dissolved. The sessions afflicted him with boredom or *taedium vitae,* as he expressed it in a letter to Mme. Raffalovich. His connection with government affairs was apparently not active enough for him to take part in debates, even on such subjects as academic freedom or public medical service in rural districts. That he was regarded as a staunch supporter of the administration is indicated by his appointment on a committee to bring in an amendment to the constitution giving the Emperor unrestricted choice in nominations to the Senate, removing the previous provision for consultation with his ministers. In his political opinions, at least, Bernard had not submitted to the influence of that ardent republican, Magendie.

Additional evidence of the nature of these opinions occurs in the collection of random reflections published posthumously by Delhoume under the title of *Pensées*. This material came from two notebooks of the same sort as *The Red Notebook,* but later in date, and certainly subsequent to the publication of the *Introduction*. They are the best substitute we have for a personal diary, and record, not events, but Bernard's ideas as they first occurred to him, before they had been censored and marshalled for use in a book or lecture. Early in their acquaintance Bernard wrote to Mme. Raffalovich: "I have so far not found anyone except you who has put a finger on this intellectual shortcoming of mine; . . . to put something into words without developing it enough to make it completely comprehensible." He spoke also of "larvae of ideas" which had to go through metamorphoses to achieve their final butterfly state.

Intermingled with these general reflections were experimental ideas which have been segregated by Delhoume under the heading *Detached Notes.* For instance, there are memoranda to try "artificial circulations" on various organs and tissues which suggest the later work of Carrel and Lindbergh on perfusion. The proportion of random reflection to physiology in *Pensées* is about one to three.

A few pronouncements on politics are included. Bernard would have liked to see politics reduced to a science:

> Even politics should become experimental some day, but it would have to be an observational science first, and it is not even that yet. Even when it grasps the laws of political and historical phenomena, it will not be able to control them.
>
> It will be able to attain this end only by *physical* procedures, by controlling diet, hygiene; it will render individuals moral. Today, instead of this, given over to empiricism, it promotes drunkenness and the abuse of tobacco to collect taxes.
>
> It is overwhelming to contemplate the unprecedented complexity of this science. Still it is conceivable. Liberty stops where science begins, as Lemoine says.

In another passage he compared historical progress with the continuance of organic life by means of the constant development of new primitive cells:

> The civilization of a nation is a movement toward death. The upper classes do not go down again. There must always be primitive or barbarous men who become civilized and rise. If this renewal does not take place, society dies like an organism deprived of cellular renewal.

This observation is natural from a Frenchman two generations after the first great European revolution which attempted to exterminate a class.

Another passage takes an almost fatalistic view of our political destiny:

> Men do act on a very limited scale; but they do not act on great events. In history, in politics, for example: in medicine, epidemics, the appearance of parasites, etc., there are *currents*. We are carried away by them, we must follow them, try not to break our necks, not to drown as we do when we are swept away in a stream.
>
> There is a great social current which is carrying humanity to its doom, with the formula of equality which does not exist in nature, but the current is there and we cannot escape it.

Nothing could be clearer than that the man who wrote this did not have the temperament of a revolutionary. It agrees quite well, however, with Bernard's acquiescent but inactive behavior under a regime like that of the Second Empire.

13

THE WAR OF 1870–1871

All I can tell you is that the Prussians will be on my mind until they are off French soil. Letter to Mme. Raffalovich, 1870.

THE ONLY SUGGESTION THAT BERNARD WAS AWARE OF THE ominous state of diplomatic relations between France and Germany in 1869 was the delay of his customary departure for Saint-Julien at the end of the summer by his conscientious attendance in the Senate. He finally escaped in the middle of September, leaving Chevreul, who at eighty-three was resolved on no account to stir out of Paris, to preside in his stead at the Academy of Sciences. He took with him an analysis of a book which Mme. Raffalovich had sent him from Munich where she was on holiday. He wrote to her that the thought of Munich revived his old dream of a trip to Germany and visits to Liebig, Bischoff, Pettenkoffer, and Voit; however, he was quite sure that it would remain "only a dream."

In reply to her request for an account of his country place, he sent the description of the Beaujolais landscape which has become so well known through Renan's reproduction of it. The rest of his letter dealt with his immediate activities:

> The vintage has commenced since my arrival and it is not over yet. Every day I get up at six o'clock, go down to the vats, and superintend the fermentation and the pressing. During the day I go to the vineyards, oversee the workers, while I inspect the vines. I have six vatfuls to make, which is the equivalent of about 160 or 170 barrels of wine; there are two already pressed, two in process of fermentation, and for two the grapes are still to be gathered. Today I am having the grapes in the yard around the house gathered, and as I write I see the vintagers from my window. You see, my dear madam, that for the time being I am transformed into a winegrower. These are the occupations which are familiar to me, and in the midst of which I was born; they always give me pleasure and they are certainly much more agreeable to me than composing academic discourses. The wine this year will be of excellent quality.
>
> At the end of the month the vintage will be over. The mountain vintagers will climb back to their homes, the country will lose its animation, and I shall be left in solitude. I do not dread it, quite the contrary. I have the whole month of October in which to surrender myself freely to tranquil reflection; for me that is supreme happiness. Then I shall sell my wines and leave for Paris to dive, as someone has said, into that abyss of vexation and misery, and so on to the end.

In her first enthusiasm as collaborator Mme. Raffalovich sent more translations and résumés than Bernard found time to read. He reminded her that he was on holiday from physiology but softened the rebuke with compliments. He said the notes he had read were clear and comprehensive and she had displayed qualities of mind not usually found together, "logical firmness and delicacy of feeling."

As time went on he made a habit of "setting aside" for her all the books and articles in German, English, and

Italian which came to hand. Her daughter Sophie helped with English and her sister, Mme. de Chaptal, with Italian. Bernard would write: "I forgot to thank you for the translation of (Wilhelm) His's opuscule. . . . If it is not abusing your kindness and boring you, I should like to have all the author's ideas on morphology." Or: "I am very grateful to you for having sent the translation of Cyon. If it is not too tiring or too long, I should like to know the end because I have come to the conclusion that curare is a very great source of error in experiments of this kind." Or: "Your judgment and characterization of Ludwig is a masterpiece of criticism. I compliment you on it." This last causes regret that Mme. Raffalovich's letters were destroyed, for it would have been interesting to know in what judgment of his great contemporary Bernard so enthusiatically concurred.

Mme. Raffalovich took more initiative in philosophical matters, accepting Bernard's invitations to comment upon his views and recommending contemporary philosophers to him. "Let me have the rest about Herbert Spencer," wrote Bernard; "what you have sent me interests me keenly." He asked for a more complete account of the psychologist Alexander Bain, although he supposed that John Stuart Mill would be "more in your line." He deferred to her judgment of the clearness with which he had expressed his own opinions but when she accused him of a mixed metaphor or a doubtful grammatical construction, he defended himself stoutly. "After all, there is such a thing as poetic license; in my capacity as academician I may perhaps be allowed some grammatical license." After a discussion about the meanings of *disillusionment* and *deception* he wrote: "Thanks to you I have become very expert on this subject and I hope that on a dictionary day it may win me some honor in the Academy."

As the holiday at Saint-Julien drew to a close Bernard

reluctantly began to reread his *Report* with Mme. Raffalovich's notes on it. The publisher Hachette was "impatiently waiting" for Bernard's revisions for a second edition. He in the end abandoned the idea of "developing a number of points which are barely sketched in the old edition," deciding to let the new one come out with "few or no changes." He began to plan his course at the College of France, lately resumed after so long an interruption: "The work I am taking up again . . . has a fresh attraction for me. I am like an exile who returns to his country and finds there the only consolations that are left him."

Back in Paris at the end of October, he was oppressed by the demands of his return to an active academic life. He caught cold but began work nevertheless on a research problem on asphyxia and went with Mme. Raffalovich to her box at the *Comédie Française*. He sketched a typical day:

> Yesterday as I was going out at half-past twelve, the concierge gave me your note, I put it in my pocket, ran from the College of France to the Botanical Gardens where the Minister of Education was to meet us, from there to the Academy of Sciences where I read a memoir, from there to the competition at the Medical School, and finally home, where I could read your letter while I had dinner.

In December he opened his course at the College of France on anesthesia and asphyxia, but dissuaded Mme. Raffalovich from attending it, since he was sure she would not like "pure physiology." To have her come would be like taking a guest into the kitchen to see the dishes prepared, the College of France being only the kitchen of science, as he had said in his *Introduction*. The winter course of 1869–1870 did in fact return to his earlier manner of keeping a close connection between the lectures and his current experiments, differing from the general discussions of method which he gave early in 1869 when Mme. Raffalovich first heard him.

Half way through the course, he was obliged to attend a ball at the Tuilleries and confessed that he had been "horribly bored and tired." A little later when there was another court ball and an invitation to dine with Mme. Raffalovich on the same evening, he chose the dinner. He went out a good deal this winter. Among other invitations was one to the house of Mme. Ancelot, widow of an Academician and mother-in-law of the celebrated defence counsel for Mme. Lafarge, Charles Lachaud; notable herself, moreover, for her earlier successes as a playwright. It would be interesting to know whether Bernard was invited as an Academician or a known devotee of the theatre. At the reception, without his knowledge, he was being observed by a young connection of the household, Arsène d'Arsonval, who was in Paris to attend the Sainte-Barbe school. From this occasion young d'Arsonval, who was to play an important part in Bernard's last years, recalled him as "an Olympian of very fine presence, but quite simple in manners and bearing."

The most important official occurrence of 1870 was his inaugural lecture at the Museum of Natural History in June. At the beginning of the year he had asked for 400,000 francs as an endowment for his work there. It was not forthcoming, the Emperor being reported to have commented that "physiology costs as much as artillery." The lectures on "The Method and Principles of Physiology" were well received, and were abstracted for the *Revue scientifique* by a new secretarial aid, Lemaistre, who had scarcely accomplished this task before he was called up for ambulance service and later killed.

The incident of the Spanish succession reached its crisis in France's declaration of war on Germany July 19, 1870.

Bernard went directly from the Senate to the Raffaloviches to announce the Ministry's decision. Sophie Raffalovich related that her mother burst into tears and that Bernard was taken aback and repeated the Minister of War's declaration, "But we are ready!" His momentary confidence was soon changed to foreboding:

> The war is beginning, who knows where it will take us. I can only bend my head before the storm of events which sweeps over the wills of men. Man believes because he is in the midst of events that he directs them; he is only their instrument.

The Raffaloviches withdrew to Trouville, and when the war news became grave early in August, Bernard wrote urging them not to return, "although the fortification and state of siege of Paris" was not "a real cause for alarm." He himself, while "deeply moved and uneasy over the unhappy turn of events," was "not discouraged." He wished he had his health and were thirty years younger, so that he could "go to the front." As things were, he could merely stick to his post in the Senate. He went there and to the Academy of Sciences assiduously, but found he could not work in his laboratory.

That he had some thoughts of an eventual retreat is suggested by his preparation of jars for collecting at the seaside "some animals which I have for a long time been planning to study." Since he had previously told Mme. Raffalovich that Brittany was much too far away for a holiday, it clearly required an invasion to turn his thoughts to the seashore. He occupied himself with rearranging his laboratory at the College of France, and when some new bookcases, previously ordered, arrived at his flat, he spent time sorting and rearranging his books.[1] He tried the bizarre distraction of paying a visit to see alive, as he said, a person who had bequeathed to him his body for experimental purposes, and was disappointed to find the testator not quite sane. He continued doggedly to go to the Senate, and was there on Sunday, September 4, when the news of the fall of Sedan and the capture of the Emperor precipitated the proclamation of the Third Republic. Before the end of the day he wrote to Mme. Raffalovich:

> The newspapers will inform you of the events and the swift catastrophe which have plunged the country into an abyss. Invasion and revolution in its wake! I have just left the Senate, its last sitting, doubtless; the Legislature was invaded with the old cry . . . "Long live the Republic!" . . . The deputies were dispersed and could no longer deliberate. Delirium has set in.

While urging Mme. Raffalovich to remain away from Paris, Bernard at first resolved to stay in the city himself. He went to the Academy of Sciences on September 5 and presented a paper by Jousset de Bellesme on scorpion venom. On the following evening he attended the regular bimonthly dinner of Parisian intellectuals at the café Brébant, where the conversation was recorded by the Goncourts. Berthelot prophesied the burning of Paris by the Prussians, averring that petrol had already been thrown into the Seine. Renan refused to subscribe to the general condemnation of the German people and, although he

[1] Bernard's library at his death consisted of 1,275 volumes, all scientific and medical works except the novels of Balzac and de Champfleury (whom Bernard must have made the mistake of collecting instead of Flaubert), and Brillat-Savarin's *Physiology of Taste,* a gourmet's mélange of essays and recipes.

later denied it, was understood to say that they were a superior race.

At the Academy of Sciences only aspects of science related to the war were now considered worthy of discussion. Surgical procedures and the threat of famine were the timely themes. Bernard presented a note by Rabuteau, recommending a mixed infusion of coffee, tea, cocoa, and sugar, a few grams of which daily, it was maintained, would support life for some months. It was proposed that the formula be sent to the besieged cities.

On September 27 he wrote to Mme. Raffalovich, now at Marseilles, that he had arrived at Saint-Julien "by endless detours," spending ten days on the way. Later he explained his decision to leave Paris:

> I encountered annoyances and obstacles which showed me that I could have no part to play for the public good; and besides, under the influence or moral causes, no doubt, a sudden attack of my illness, which I thought I was done with, but which has only been dormant, made its appearance, and I decided abruptly to leave Paris. It was the 15th or 16th of September when I was still able to leave, by the last train to go, I think.

The governor of Paris was in fact urging noncombatants to leave the city as the Germans approached. Bernard had gone to Bourges the first day and stayed the night with friends near Montluçon, who kept him longer when they saw how ill he was. When news arrived that the trains were going through to Lyons, he set out on the final leg of his journey.

He remained at Saint-Julien for the rest of 1870 and the first five months of 1871. At various times he contemplated further retreat before the Prussians to Cannes or, following the tide of events, a return to Paris. Mme. Raffalovich invited him to join her family at Nice, and later at Fribourg in Switzerland, but he stayed at Saint-Julien. The mayor of that village, when it seemed that the Germans might occupy Lyons, asked Bernard if he knew any of the doctors in the German army. Bernard did not commit himself to the mayor but wrote to Mme. Raffalovich that he had no taste for staying on if it meant "being amiable to the Prussians." He had no scruples about using such expressions as "the barbarians from Berlin" and, later on, "the odious conqueror." However, he wrote also that, with some unspecified reservations, he approved of Renan's statement in the September *Revue des deux mondes* that war between France and Germany was the greatest misfortune which could befall civilization, and his proposal of a European federation which would stand above all nationalities.

Until the end of November there was nothing to diminish the strain of his anxiety. The fall of Metz and the revolutionary disorders of October had only heightened it. As he wrote to Mme. Raffalovich, he grew tired of reading the adverb *revolutionarily* in the papers from Lyons: "Revolutionarily; it is the fashionable word. I have learned: they proceed only revolutionarily; they speak, march, fight, revolutionarily; they dress, drink, and eat, revolutionarily. . . . I desist because we have agreed to put politics aside between us."

Mme. Raffalovich viewed the occurrences in Paris more sympathetically than Bernard. She had been an ardent Republican even under the Empire and kept in touch with political exiles like Armand Barbès and Edgar Quinet. Bernard remarked that her democratic opinions were not altogether in keeping with her talk of recruiting a staff for the new flat she was to have on the fashionable avenue de la reine Hortense after the war. Even he, however, was moved to cry, "Long live the Republic, one and indivisible!" when Gambetta's activities led to the first sortie out of Paris on November 28, and the successes of the army of the Loire.

The winter began in earnest at Saint-Julien in December. There was a foot of snow and what Bernard called "twelve degrees of cold," with radiant sunshine in the daytime and a brilliant moon at night. He wrote of the cold in terms of the suffering it would bring to the armies in the field. His solitary walks were curtailed. He read all the papers and his letters discussing the national catastrophe were despatched every week or oftener. He used his father's desk, "the handles of which have remained twisted and bent since the invasion of 1815."

Mme. Raffalovich tried to recall his thoughts to science. When he admitted that he had "never read the many works of Voit on nutrition because they were in German," she translated and sent him accounts of some of the chief experiments. Only an "Ouf!" at the end indicated that it had been a considerable task. He at once wrote to thank her and apologize for having involved her in anything "so diluted and unnutritious as the thin theories of Messieurs Voit and Liebig." Nevertheless he had enjoyed reading the translations and had adorned the margins with "reflections on experimental projects" which occurred to him.

When the disorder in Marseilles threatened to spread to Nice, Mme. Raffalovich asked Bernard's opinion of Montpellier as a possible refuge and he confessed that he knew nothing of the second great medical center of France except what he had seen from the train. His acquaintance with the faculty was "very casual." When he wrote on Christmas day the Raffaloviches were still in Nice for he contrasted the "six feet" of snow in which he was now imbedded with the winter flowers of that resort. He could only sit at the window and look at nature "wrapped in a great, sad shroud." Nothing living could be seen except a few starved blackbirds silhouetted against the snow as they hunted for frozen hawthorn berries.

In an early January letter, Mme. Raffalovich found fault with "the indifference of the provinces." Bernard replied that, as a temporary provincial himself, he understood why many country people believed Paris to be at the bottom of all their political misfortunes, when "a dozen suburbanites could overthrow the government and impose their will on all the rest of France." He looked for a movement away from centralization after the war. He was now "snowed in" and reduced to walking up and down his room "like a caged bear." The oldest winegrowers had never seen so much snow. He added that at the time of writing his fire had gone out and he was frozen. He was driven to reading novels, which annoyed him because they "all have the same ending." He usually composed his mind before going to bed by reading a page or two from Pascal's *Pensées,* or from the reflections of that other seventeenth-century moralist, Nicole.

On the last day of January rumors of an armistice were afloat. Bernard, who had expressed willingness "to hold out for ten years, if necessary," thought the Republic had gained little by the resistance, great as his patriotic approval of it had been. He commented also on rumors that the Paris apartments of evacuees were being requisitioned for those whose dwellings had been shelled. He expressed good-humored annoyance at the prospect of fraternizing with these unfortunates, and hoped that they would not try to keep warm by burning his books and papers.

When the news of the armistice of January 28 became official, he called the peace "shameful and disastrous." He distributed the blame impartially among "the negligence of the Empire, the ineptitude of the Republic, and the odious hypocrisy of Prussia." The first rumors had brought on a crisis "of his entrails," which had left him hypersensitive and irritable; when they were confirmed, he "walked up and down the whole day long with a feeling of distress" forewarning him of a fresh attack. "When shall I be rid of this accursed affliction," he wrote despairingly. Recovering a little, he began to consider a return to Paris, but although some trains were running, passengers were warned that they might not go through. It did not reassure him to learn that absent professors were being put on the index and their salaries stopped.

He was a little encouraged by the first signs of spring. The primroses showed green leaves and the coltsfoot its first buds. He noticed that the fields were silent; there were no birds that year except a small screech owl which sat on the chimney in the evening, uttering its cry, "like a long harmonious moan." Bernard's mind suddenly went back thirty years and he remembered a vaudeville he had seen at the *Palais-Royal* when he was still a medical student. A romantic poet with elaborately disheveled hair had come on the stage to recite his own verses:

Quoi de plus touchant
Que le chant
De la chouette
Qui *hue* au haut de la tour muette.[2]

Bernard was astonished to find what he unkindly called "these crude rhymes" buried at the bottom of his skull for so long. He decided that "a human being is an odd machine."

By the middle of February the countryside had come to

---

[2] What is more poignant than the owl's moan as it calls "who-oo" atop the silent tower.

life. Bernard reported meeting the mayor and his neighbor of the chateau de Montmelas, now "citizen Tournon," formerly the Marquis de Tournon de Montmelas, descendant of the feudal lords of Saint-Julien. The Marquis urged Bernard to call on his daughter-in-law, the Countess de Tournon, whose husband was with the forces besieged in Belfort. When Bernard did so a month later he found the Countess gone to meet her husband, escorted by one of the des Garets (the family to which the Abbé des Garets, benefactor of Bernard's youth, belonged). The old marquis entertained him with "endless tales."

On February 16 Pasteur came to Saint-Julien. He had been in his native Jura during the war, having left Paris ten days before Bernard in 1870, but had emerged to look for his son in the army of the East. After finding the boy, not wounded, but ill from privation, and taking him to recuperate at Geneva, he returned to visit his brother-in-law, Dean of the Faculty of Sciences at Lyons, whence he traveled to see Bernard.

There was plenty of news to exchange. Bernard had just learned that neither his apartment nor his quarters at the College of France had been damaged, although shells had struck both the house and the College. The situation at the Normal School had been much more serious; one wing was demolished and forty soldiers were still quartered in Pasteur's laboratory. The two scientists must surely have discussed Chevreul's defiance of the enemy. The morning after the Museum of Natural History had been shelled, he appeared before the Academy of Sciences to read a declaration that this desecration of the garden of medicinal plants founded by edict of Louis XIII in 1629 had occurred in the reign of William I of Prussia. Pasteur had been so moved by Chevreul's protest that, on January 18, he sent back to the University of Bonn the diploma for his honorary doctorate in medicine because it bore the signature of King William of Prussia.

Bernard held no German honorary degrees, but since the early sixties he had been an honorary member of the Academy of Sciences of Berlin, as well as of all the other important scientific societies of Europe, from the Royal Society of London to the Academy of St. Petersburg, and from Stockholm to Constantinople. He made no gestures at this time, and expressed to Mme. Raffalovich a certain understanding of the patriotism of the Dean at Bonn, who rebuked Pasteur for his insult to the German nation in the "Sacred Person" of its sovereign, adding that the Dean probably in his heart agreed that the "Sacred Personage is only an old beast who has been persuaded that he wins all the battles."

On his return to Lyons, Pasteur prepared an article for its *Salut public* under the title, "Why France Lacked Outstanding Men in Her Moment of Peril." After reviewing the distinguished history of French science during the Revolution and under Napoleon, including its contribution to the art of war, he accused later administrations of neglecting higher education. Bernard had expressed privately to Mme. Raffalovich the view that France had lost the war to Germany because the French masses lacked "scientific sense." He added:

> You are right, dear madam; under the monarchy the elections are republican, under the Republic the elections are monarchical; and then when we are under a monarchy once more, the elections will be republican again, and so on to the end. It is the consequence of this spirit of revolt against things as they are which breathes over France and which has driven her in pursuit of the best form of government for eighty years. I think the malady goes very deep, it has diverse causes, and it might not be

impossible that some day I should say what I think on this subject in regard to matters within my competence.

Fortunately, perhaps, Bernard never carried out this threat and confined his political reflections to his private notebooks and his correspondence. His expectation that France would be "under a monarchy once more" was shared, it must be remembered, by the largest party in the Assembly which had been elected to make peace with Germany. He said, half in jest, half in apology, that he must seem like a "misanthrope who fails to appreciate his good luck in living under the Republic." He did not like the disorders or the retributive measures of the new regime. "I could tell you of some odious and heart-rending things which have happened in my own district," he wrote to Mme. Raffalovich. He said it was a "disillusion" when Paul Bert, on whom he had "founded scientific hopes," accepted the prefecture of the North; "if he wants to be a prefect, it is not the fire of science which animates him." He told Bert himself, "My poor Bert, since you entered politics, you have become a man who affirms, that is to say, you have ceased to be a man of science."

At the beginning of March the new Assembly accepted Bismarck's conditions, which Bernard, like every other Frenchman, regarded as humiliating and disastrous. He considered the government which had made it "unprincipled," and was convinced that the enormous indemnity of five billion francs would never be paid. He was even more indignant over the failure of the government to suppress the insurrection and terrorism which continued in Paris throughout February and March, and decided not to attempt to return to the capital until order was reestablished. In February, he was told, there was no light at night in Paris, and no cabs by day, and he would run the risk of having to carry his baggage on his back from the station. At the beginning of April he was warned that there was security for no one. An old schoolfellow was killed in the street fighting. When a long letter he had written Mme. Raffalovich, freely criticizing the provisional government, had apparently not reached her, he feared it had been officially intercepted.

In spite of the disorders the Raffaloviches returned to Paris in the middle of March. Mme. Raffalovich had proposed a visit to Saint-Julien to break the journey from Nice. Bernard had looked up trains and suggested a lunch of "fresh eggs and a cutlet, it won't matter for once." He sent to Villefranche for replacements of his six yew trees which had been killed by the severe winter. He wanted to be informed of the exact time of his guests' arrival because a carriage from the station might be difficult to find as a result of the government's requisitions of horses. In the end Mme. Raffalovich decided that it would be too difficult and Bernard was left with his jonquils and his violets "making haste to bloom," their "homage disdained."

In the middle of April he began a round of farewell calls in the neighborhood and accepted an invitation to dine at the chateau de Montmelas. In May he was startled by the announcement that the Raffalovich family might return to Odessa. He wrote hoping that he would not be deprived of the happiness of seeing *madame* again, and added that his admiration for her was very great. As it turned out, the idea of going to Odessa was abandoned, and Mme. Raffalovich went no farther than Heidelberg. When she invited him to join her, he declined on the ground that a French scientist would not yet be welcome in Germany. He said that he was "hungry and thirsty for Paris" and had "an indigestion of the country." He was nervous and depressed and in June ill once more. Nevertheless he wrote to the director of the Botanical Gardens and the administration of the College of France expressing willingness to return to his posts at two weeks notice.

He returned to Paris on June 9, 1871, on hearing that some courses at the College of France would reopen on the 12th. His own lectures were not resumed until November at the Museum and January, 1872, at the College of France. He was nevertheless soon "working seriously," spending two or three days a week at his experiments. He wrote: "My ardor for science is the same as ever; I think that my spirit is what it used to be, but my strength betrays me. Two days ago (in July) I experimented for five hours at a stretch and I still feel worn out. Alas! Youth has flown and in future my plans will have to drag a chain which will grow heavier and heavier."

The French Academy welcomed his return by electing him its chancellor. His routine "nailed" him to Paris for the summer. Letters to Heidelberg were despatched every few days, and mentioned the probable annoyance with which Prussia might be expected to receive the news of the success of the French loan to pay off the indemnity and end the occupation. Bernard also remarked acidly on the unwillingness of the Count de Chambord to give up the symbol of the Bourbon white in exchange for a throne. When the Orleanist party had withdrawn its support from the Count de Paris to gain unanimity in the royalist ranks, the legitimist heir had objected to the continued use of the national red, white, and blue. The Count's ancestor, Henry IV, had given up his religion, Bernard remarked, to become king of France; the prospective Henry V should not have balked at giving up a flag.

Bernard's last tasks before leaving for Saint-Julien in September were a visit to the Minister of Education (for assurance that funds would be provided for his laboratory), and his preface for the volume of his 1859–1860 lectures, which had been translated back into French from Benjamin Ball's English rendering. Baillière was publishing them with a series of lectures on the spinal cord and a selection of others on general topics, under the title of *Experimental Pathology*. He had been petitioning Bernard for the corrected proofs and the preface since April. In the preface Bernard indicates the place of this volume in the design for the *Principles of Medicine,* which had a little prematurely been described as "in the press" on the flyleaf of the *Introduction*. "The point which I sought to emphasize," he wrote, "was that pathology and physiology should not be studied in isolation."

The journey to Saint-Julien was enlivened by Bernard's ejection from the compartment for "ladies only" which he had entered by mistake and the companionship in his new compartment of a family of American tourists, father, mother, son, and daughter, of whom only the daughter spoke French. In spite of having already lunched at the station restaurant at Tonnerre, Bernard was asked to share the dessert from an enormous lunch basket of roast chicken and fruit. With the daughter as interpreter Bernard carried on a highly technical conversation with the father about the quality of different French wines and the details of their exportation.

He stayed in Saint-Julien just long enough to supervise the vintage, and returned to Paris in time to accompany Mme. Raffalovich in October to the ceremony marking the reinstallation of the glass broken at the Botanical Gardens during the bombardment. To judge from his letters, the ceremony marked the end of the Franco-Prussian war for Bernard.

14

GENERAL PHYSIOLOGY AT THE MUSEUM (1872–1875)

Wherever life exists, the processes of organic synthesis and destruction go on simultaneously. Phenomena of Life Common to Animals and Plants.

THE CONSTRUCTIVE WORK WHICH BERNARD WAS STILL TO DO was in the field of general physiology. During his years at the Museum he founded this part of his science. His contributions went back to his teaching at the Sorbonne and to the proof of the universality of starch (glycogen being an animal starch), but the synthesis of his ideas was accomplished in his lectures at the Museum from 1872 to 1876. In July, 1871, he announced to Mme. Raffalovich as the subject of his autumn lectures "The Phenomena of Life Common to Animals and Plants." The phrase was used for all his subsequent lectures at the Museum and as the title of his posthumously published book, *Phénomènes de la vie communs aux animaux et aux végétaux,* henceforward to be referred to as the *Phenomena.* This two volume work collected the Museum lectures, but not in the order in which they were delivered. Bernard had literally built up his conclusions as he lectured and his definitive views were expressed only in the course of 1876, which was used for the first chapters of the book as summary of its principles and plan.

The problems of the Museum lectures were reflective rather than experimental, but in the postwar years there was a marked revival of experimental activity in both Bernard's laboratories. Although the College of France was still his headquarters, he was making ample use of the Botanical Gardens, "guarded by the wolves" of the neighboring zoo, where he enjoyed better hygienic conditions for work than ever before.

He had no lack of competent aid during the early seventies since Gréhant, Ranvier, and Dastre all served him as assistants. Many of the experiments, however, were carried out by his own hands, and he could scarcely bear to leave his new incubator, his crayfish ("delightful, interesting creatures"), and his Alpine marmots, even for his customary holidays. His renewed activity was directed toward the filling in of detail in researches on animal heat (the marmots), diabetes and glycogenesis (the crayfish), asphyxia and anesthesia (where he was to make his most significant observation of this period), all subjects going back to his earliest experimentation.

The seventies also saw a restoration of his early relationship with the Society of Biology. He not only resumed the duties of presiding officer, but communicated to the Society, rather than to the Academy of Sciences, the fresh findings on old subjects gathered in his current researches.

His position as the foremost scientist of France was recognized when, in January, 1872, he was chosen the first president of the recently organized French Association for the Advancement of Science (A.F.A.S.). The flame of national patriotism had been fanned by military defeat, and it was felt that French scientists should stand together. Bernard's health prevented him from presiding at the first session at Bordeaux in September, 1872, but he made up for it in 1873, 1875, and 1876 by acting as chairman of his section, reading papers, and giving demonstrations. He avoided engagements which took him away from Paris. Only his devotion to science in its national aspect carried him to meetings in provincial cities like Lyons, Nantes, and Clermont-Ferrand.

In December, 1871, his lectures at the College of France on animal heat were interrupted by a brief illness, but he was able to resume them in January, 1872. He amused himself in his convalescence by watching from his window four young chimney-sweeps making a slide in the snow. They reminded him of the blackbirds against the snow at Saint-Julien the year before. Although he never suffered another complete breakdown until his final illness, and although in the seventies he put on flesh and had a better color, his letters bear witness to constant colds in the winter and spring, to attacks of neuralgia, and eventually sciatica, severe enough to make walking difficult. He was more and more inclined to open "the big umbrella of refusals" against "the storm of invitations," but he was faithful to old friends, refusing to be one of those who ceased to wait upon Princess Mathilde after her return from retirement at Enghien to the rue de Berry. He considered himself really ill only when his lecture schedule was interrupted.

He relied upon Mme. Raffalovich for translations of current articles which would "do for tomorrow's lecture." He no longer felt equal to "extemporaneous research before the public," which demanded "an effort and intensity of work of which I am no longer capable." However, on the last day of the spring course, with a large audience present, Bernard, as he put it, "made a discovery in the middle of the lecture." "The public and I were enchanted with our success." He was describing the part played by body heat in recovery from carbon monoxide poisoning, and it occurred to him that muscular contraction played a part in the process. He devised an experiment to illustrate this, which, he said, "succeeded perfectly." He was quite jubilant in reporting the incident to Mme. Raffalovich and he still thought well enough of it three years later to put it as a footnote to his account of carbon monoxide in his *Anesthetics and Asphyxia,* which came out a year before his *Animal Heat.* His result, however, was less conclusive than he had imagined. He was premature in saying, "It will be a closed question."

He caught the attention of the public again that same March when he published in the *Revue des deux mondes* an article on "The Function of the Brain." His thesis was that the phenomena of consciousness and intelligence were the result of the functioning of the organ which expresses them, that this organ was dependent upon physiological conditions, and that its functioning could be investigated by the same methods as those used for any other organ of the body. He was a little contemptuous of the resulting hubbub in the Academy between "the Voltaireans and freethinkers" and "the others." "I am by intention," he said, "neither materialist nor spiritualist. I give small thought to where the truth will lead me, provided that I find it."

He found the amateur philosophy of Chevreul more congenial when he visited him with Mme. Raffalovich (at her request) a little later in the spring at the Museum of Natural History. Chevreul had been the first to direct Bernard's attention to the need for defining just what is meant, under different circumstances, by calling something a fact. Speaking as a chemist, Chevreul insisted that a fact was an abstraction. Bernard could see that some "facts," *e.g.,* that there is sugar in the blood, were generalizations or abstractions; but he also thought that the facts with which a physiologist was more particularly concerned were better described as "material acts" of the experimental subject, and Chevreul graciously conceded that some sciences were less directly addressed to the abstract than others. Bernard was perhaps feeling his way toward the conception of an *event,* fundamental to the view of the modern realist Whitehead.

Bernard had a high opinion of Chevreul's acumen. "It would take at least a Chevreul," he wrote to Mme. Raffalovich, "to show us an Ariadne's thread to help us find our way in this labyrinth called the human heart." In the seventies it became Bernard's habit to call upon Chevreul in his rooms at the Museum on Sunday afternoons, where he also frequently met his friends the Barrals, father and son. Chevreul's conversation, which drew upon the reminiscences of his long lifetime (already half way through his eighties, he was destined to live to be one hundred and three), was always diverting, but at about this time was focussed on the published correspondence of Napoleon. Bernard was fascinated by these letters which, he insisted, "revealed the man a thousand times better than all the conflicting judgments of his contemporaries." The great drawback to visiting Chevreul, especially in winter, was that his large reception room, heated only by a narrow eighteenth-century fireplace, was likely to be very chilly. It was also difficult to interrupt the old gentleman long enough for the courtesies of leavetaking. Bernard had found that the best way to manage this was to slip a pun[1] into the conversation which Chevreul would invari-

[1] Examples of Bernard's puns besides the well known "Sisyphe-six ifs" are: "faisans bienfaisans" or "bene*ficent pheasants*" of a brace of pheasants given him by the Baroness de Rothschild and passed on by him to the Raffaloviches; and "L'Eveque, Brulé, Enfer, Du-

ably pause to ponder over, so that Bernard could seize the opportunity to rise and begin his farewells.

Bernard's lectures at the Museum in the early summer of 1872 were the first of those eventually collected for publication in the *Phenomena.* They can now be found in the first two parts of the second volume, in which the discovery of glycogen, or "animal starch," is treated as a contribution to general physiology. Bernard considered that he had disproved the doctrine of "vital duality," which attributed the function of organic synthesis to plants, leaving only the breaking down of nutritive materials to the animal kingdom. He thought that his demonstration that animals can derive sugar from a protein diet entitled him to say that "sugar is produced in the animal by a mechanism identical with that which operates in the plant."

What he really meant was that in both the animal and vegetable kingdoms the same relationship held between starch, the form in which energy is stored, and sugar, the form in which energy is immediately available for nutrition. He was quite aware that, through the agency of chlorophyl, plants build up starch from carbon dioxide and water by means of energy from the sun, which is therefore the ultimate source of energy for all living things. He was quite right in his main contention that "in spite of the actual variety which vital phenomena display in their outward manifestation, they are fundamentally the same in plants and animals, because the nutrition of vegetable and animal cells, the only essential living parts, cannot have a different mode of existence in the two king-

---

bois" (The bishop burnt in hell with wood) purporting to be a list of the names of municipal officials who negotiated with the invading Germans.

doms." It is true that while a green plant is in sunshine, the more conspicuous process is the one which involves the giving off of oxygen and the consumption of carbon dioxide, in the manufacture of starch. But at the same time the reverse (and the true respiratory) process, which involves the consumption of oxygen and the giving off of carbon dioxide, is also going on, and becomes the more conspicuous process in darkness. Bernard was concerned to emphasize the identity of the essential metabolic processes in the two kingdoms. He was always more interested in qualitative than quantitative aspects of biochemical reactions, and had been inclined to leave the field of energy relationships in the hands of his German contemporaries, Helmholtz, Pettenkoffer, and Voit. His treatment of the subject rather neglects the significant energy contribution of green plants to the other forms of life.

In May he took time off to attend, with the physicist Victor Regnault, the posthumous exhibition of paintings by Regnault's son Henri, killed in the last sortie out of Paris in 1871. Visits to the galleries and Salons had been a favorite recreation for Bernard ever since he had discovered the Louvre in his first year in Paris. He mentions in the letters his attraction to Ribera and Murillo, but de Gleyre, who painted Mme. Raffalovich, is the only contemporary artist referred to besides young Regnault. If one may venture upon a pun in Bernard's own manner, the Impressionists failed to make an impression. Of Regnault, with whose work he had been familiar since the artist's father had shown him early sketches, he said rather ingenuously: "He was certainly destined to become one of the glories of France in his art."

Bernard's own ideas of design are alarmingly illustrated by the plans he made for a frontispiece for his *Principles of Experimental Medicine*. His description runs: "At the end of a portico was a doorway above which appeared nature symbolically represented. She was a splendid woman, peacefully asleep, while all the beasts of creation swarmed around her to draw nourishment from her bounteous breasts. The plans and the books in which the materials for this frontispiece are to be found were left with the artist."

An absorbing interest in his resumed experiments kept Bernard in the city after his Museum course was over and in spite of the summer heat. While engaged in an experiment he incurred first-degree burns on his left hand from an explosion of alcohol which set fire to his clothes. The accident may have had something to do with his failure to come to Bordeaux to preside over the first session of the A.F.A.S.

He went down to Saint-Julien in September, taking Descartes' *Traité de l'homme (Treatise on Man* or *De Homine)* and a microscope. He was soon "overjoyed" at Mme. Raffalovich's proposal to visit him there on her way back from Italy where she was traveling with the Renans. He looked up trains and recommended the hotel *de l'Europe* in Mâcon, which, although farther away, he thought would be a better headquarters than Villefranche. He outlined his plans for a dinner party to which he had also invited the dean of the Faculty at Lyons, and sent off his letter with a few autumn violets pressed between its pages. The visit, after one postponement, finally came off in October. Bernard had been afraid that there would be no flowers or foliage left, but Mme. Raffalovich was delighted with the late autumn coloring of the Saône valley. The "rustic reception" was a complete success, its anniversary commemorated with gifts of autumn fruits or flowers in the following years.

Back in Paris, he dined with his recent guest and

brought Chevreul to call upon her. He was installed in his newly equipped laboratory at the College of France, and read the history of his chair, so as to "learn my genealogy and boast about it on occasion." He shared the regret of Renan and Berthelot over the death of Théophile Gautier, their fellow diner at the café Brébant. When, as vice-president of the College of France, he attended an official ceremony at Versailles and was received by Thiers, President of the Republic, he looked around at familiar faces, and commented: "Governments change but the office-holders remain the same; the comedy has a new title but the actors do not even change their costumes."

For the New Year of 1873 Mme. Raffalovich sent a present of a magnificent new dressing gown, bordered and lined with fur. She was inclined to munificence, and on other occasions gave him a Turkish coffee pot and a handsome early edition of Vesalius. This time, while thanking her for her "extreme kindness to one constantly subject to bad colds," he was inclined to agree with his housekeeper, Mlle. Mariette Rey, that the garment was too sumptuous to wear. Mariette's suggestion that the fur be used to line an overcoat and the silk kept for a summer dressing gown was firmly vetoed by Mme. Raffalovich.

On his return to Paris after the war Bernard had acquired the services of "mademoiselle Mariette," one of the excellent housekeepers for whom her native Auvergne was renowned. She kept the apartment at 40, rue des Écoles, in admirable order, brought Bernard lunch to the College of France if he was too busy to leave his work, earned the title of the "one-headed Cerberus" for protecting him from visitors, and nursed him when he was ill. As nurse she felt free to say that he was being properly punished for working on Sunday. She even accompanied him to Saint-Julien on his annual holiday, staying until the last week, when she took a brief vacation of her own in Auvergne, while Bernard was looked after by a niece.

Mlle. Rey was on excellent terms with the Raffaloviches and, according to Sophie, told them all her "little secrets." Bernard was in the habit of bringing back to Paris every autumn a basket of the last roses for Mme. Raffalovich, and always carried this basket himself. Mariette would put in the bottom of the basket the butter and poultry which she wished to smuggle into Paris and arrange the roses over them, selecting flowers with long stems and sharp spines. The Paris customs officials ("robbers" to Mariette) never thought of investigating the basket of a gentleman with the red ribbon of the Legion of Honor in his buttonhole. Bernard was understood to have no suspicion of the part he played in this annual affair; "his mind was elsewhere."

Bernard was too ill with a cold and neuralgia to pay his ceremonial calls on New Year's day in 1873 but was able to resume his lectures at the College of France, although he tired so easily that he devoted more and more time to demonstrations "to spare myself from talking." After the brief recess in the middle of February, he was received with applause by an unusually brilliant public, the Emperor of Brazil, dom Pedro, being among those who had applied to attend the course.

The lectures of this period ordinarily had an audience of fifty or sixty, of whom only a few were medical students. The recognized disciples, Dastre, Gréhant, Duval, Regnard, sat near the long table for experiments, and the laboratory servant, *le père* Lesage, was in attendance. The slope of the amphitheatre was filled by a varied and often cosmopolitan company. The Prince of Wales and the Count of Paris came at least once. The robes of a young Mussulman, a serious student of dissection, rivaled those of three Dominican friars who habitually took places at the top of the room. One, a passionate notetaker, was

Père Didon, later celebrated for his books on science and religion. There were also, by Bernard's own listing, priests, professors of philosophy, humanitarian dreamers, old men, young men, young women, "all wanting to know what life is."

He made a special point of describing the female auditors to Mme. Raffalovich and invented nicknames for some of them. There was the blue-eyed "periwinkle," who took him into her confidence about her matrimonial plans, the blonde Belgian "frog," a glowing young English woman, a Spanish brunette with untidy hair, an elderly Frenchwoman in spectacles, and the Russian women doctors. All these were "blue-stockings," but there were also ladies accompanied by husbands, Mme. Victor Considerant, wife of the phalansterian socialist, nun-like in black veiling, and once, high up at the end of a row, a lady described only as having very beautiful shoes and a bracelet of precious stones around her left ankle. Bernard was so fascinated by this unexpected ornament that he mistook the aorta for the carotid artery in the experimental animal, and had to apologize for his confusion, blamed his cold, coughed, and took refuge in his handkerchief.

In June he announced the end of his course at the College of France and the beginning of his lectures at the Museum, where his subject for 1873 was digestion and nutrition, eventually treated in part three of the second volume of the *Phenomena.* He pursued his theme of the essential unity of the animal and vegetable kingdoms. Nutritive materials and digestive agents were in the last analysis the same for both. "It is true," he remarked, "that there is nothing analogous to the digestive tube in a plant; but a chemical reaction is not affected by the shape of the vase. . . . Fundamentally the digestive property is nothing but the action of the ferment." The whole subject of ferments was only on the threshold of its development into the modern chemistry of enzymes. Bernard admitted that in the existing state of science it was impossible to give a final account of these agents, which he correctly defined as "nitrogen-containing organic substances which provoke the transformation of other organic substances, while themselves remaining unchanged at the end of the reaction." Nevertheless, his whole treatment of the subject seems to anticipate that such an account, when given, would remain within the boundaries of pure chemistry. This attitude was soon to bring him into conflict with his friend Pasteur, with whom he was at this very moment planning a brief, but unprecedented, excursion to Boulogne at the end of the course.

He delayed his departure a few days to see the fireworks in honor of the Shah of Persia in the Place de l'Étoile and to accept an invitation from President Thiers. Early in September he arrived in Saint-Julien. He brought Descartes and Leibnitz to read, but he wrote, "I shall probably not do them the honor of opening them; the country makes me feel intellectually indifferent." The vintage was poor that year, and his sister had just suffered the bereavement of her son's death from typhoid fever.

In 1873 the A.F.A.S. met in Lyons, where he could easily go down from Saint-Julien. It may have been in pursuance of discussions there that he turned from his proposed philosophical reading to experiments in his country laboratory. That he had not planned them before leaving Paris is suggested by his writing to Mme. Raffalovich to send him materials. His notes, headed "Saint-Julien, September-October, 1873," indicate that he was unconvinced by Pasteur's theory that fermentation depended on the living yeast being deprived of free oxygen. Bernard's experiments satisfied him that "fermentation imperatively demands the presence of air before it begins." Their general scheme was to compare grape juice exposed to the air with juice expressed and filtered out of contact with air, and kept under oil. That he considered this work merely exploratory is shown by his letter to Mme. Raffalovich: "Although I have accomplished nothing, I have nevertheless obtained some interesting results on wine fermentation. But I have not opened any book except nature's. Yet I should have liked to clear up some of the ideas of Leibnitz and Descartes."

In the same letter he said he had had a surprise visit from the blue-eyed "periwinkle" who descended upon him with a sister, an aunt, a nephew, and two small children, one of them her own. Recovering from his astonishment, he did his best to entertain them with a tour of his land, fruit, cakes, and wine. Before they left, "great plans" were made for next year. Only the "periwinkle" seems to have exercised an attraction comparable to that of Mme. Raffalovich herself.

He returned to Paris resolved to spend "a solitary winter." "Science will entirely occupy me," he explained. Irritated by an epidemic of visits from candidates aspiring to vacancies in the academies, he singled out his conversation with the historian Taine as more agreeable than the others. Editors tried to hold him to promises he had made to give them "philosophical" articles, and he had two volumes of lectures to prepare for publication.

The most important event of the year for him occurred on December 6. He had opened his course at the College of France and was lecturing on the blood, using a galvanometer to demonstrate its varying temperature in different parts of the body. The galvanometer failed to function and the demonstration was abandoned. At the end of the lecture a young man joined the group gathered around the operating table, and, after a brief inspection, indicated to Bernard what had gone wrong, and quickly restored the instrument to working order. The young man was Jacques Arsène d'Arsonval, a twenty-two-year-old medical student, and an extern at the hospital *de l'enfant Jésus.*

As soon as the audience had dispersed, Bernard took the young man across the street to his flat and, first in his study and afterwards at the lunch table, questioned him about his earlier training, his family, and his plans, the interview lasting almost the whole afternoon. D'Arsonval said afterwards that he was so encouraged by Bernard's kindly simplicity that he told his whole story, without even being aware of doing it.

He was the son and grandson of country doctors and on the way to becoming one himself. He had begun his scientific training at the Sainte-Barbe school in Paris, but when the outbreak of war sent him home to the south of France, enrolled in medicine at Limoges, where he was awarded an externship in Paris. When Bernard congratulated him on his "gift for observation," he disclosed that his family had connections with the great names in French medicine, his grandfather having been neighbor and friend of Baron Boyer and of Dupuytren, and his father voluntary *préparateur* to Laennec, a predecessor of Bernard at the College of France. Further questions revealed that young d'Arsonval's training in the physical sciences had been exceptionally thorough. When at last he reluctantly said goodbye, Bernard remarked: "Since the experiments interest you, come to see them whenever you like; it will not hinder you in preparing for your medical examinations."

Thus began the virtual adoption of a scientific heir by Bernard. The impulse which had carried the young medical student in a free hour to the celebrated lectures at the College of France was to shape his whole life. Bernard was captivated by his intelligence and charm, and impressed by his unusual grounding in the physical sciences before he had entered medicine.

Bernard did not mention this new interest to Mme. Raffalovich, who was wintering on the Riviera, but complained in an extremely illegible letter in January, 1874, that he had the toothache and his dentist was in the "Danubian principalities." The only resource he could think of was the dentist of the crocodiles at the Botanical Gardens. Some relief, whether or not on this heroic scale, must have been provided, for he was soon lamenting nothing more than his customary cold and remarking that the baroness de Rothschild had sent him a brace of pheasants.

Another basket of game in the same year prompted him to arrange an impromptu dinner party, his first at his flat. The guests included his old friend Dr. Davaine and the younger Dr. Moreau. Mlle. Mariette engaged "a pretty young girl of eighteen" to serve at table. The next day Bernard reported: "My dinner last night went off very well, but definitely, I shall not give any more. The intimacy of two suits me much better than conversation among four or five in which the mind grows weary running after ideas reflected from all sides. I am half dead this morning."

He nevertheless relented from this decision and soon afterwards gave a dinner to his laboratory assistants at the College of France.

The legend of the "scientific family" of the later seventies was dramatized in Lhermitte's painting of Bernard with the "disciples," d'Arsonval, Paul Bert, Dastre, Gréhant, Malassez, Dumontpallier (a visitor), and the laboratory servant *le père* Lesage (as we might say, Pop Lesage). Curiously, Bernard was silent about his relation with his laboratory associates; except for the remark about disappointment over Paul Bert's desertion of science for politics there is no mention of them in the letters to Mme. Raffalovich. The evidence consists of the many tributes of his pupils to his courtesy and generosity. Armand Moreau suggests that it was only the few who were able to appreciate "the demonstration of his genius" in conversations (perhaps a little one-sided, in the manner of his talk with Napoleon III), who enjoyed his society and achieved intimacy with him. The rest were content to accord him an affectionate respect. In the case of le père Lesage, the respect was idolatrous. He drove Bernard's successor at the College of France, Brown-Séquard, to desperation with his admonitions, "Claude Bernard did not operate like this; Claude Bernard thought differently."

In the letters of this winter Bernard refers twice to the current literary sensation, the posthumous publication of *Lettres à une inconnue* (Letters to an Unknown Woman) by Prosper Mérimée, better known as the author of *Carmen*. Bernard and Mme. Raffalovich shared the general curiosity about the unknown woman to whom the correspondence had been addressed. It may have struck them that there was a certain resemblance between these letters and those which they exchanged. Mérimée's letters recorded a long and devoted friendship between a writer of distinction and a woman of cultivation and charm, a relationship nourished, at least in its later stages, upon inspection of the art treasures of the Louvre and long walks in the woods at Versailles.

Bernard rather lacked the gift for contemporary gossip which secured for Mérimée his wide public. The chief value of Bernard's letters is to reveal his own personality, his humor, his shrewdness, his reflective tendency and occasional melancholy, the unexpected variety of his interests, his love of natural beauty, his strong patriotism, his sympathy, his humanity. Their style is best when conversational. His set pieces are a little self-conscious. The letters are not really intimate. There are too many compliments and no first names. However, affection is expressed in more than the concluding formulae. Justin Godart describes the relationship as "a respectful and rather sentimental attachment." Bernard admired Mme. Raffalovich's intelligence, vivacity, and charm and accepted her hero worship and her generosity. Moreover, she pleased him, because, as he frankly said, she was pretty.

A book of a very different kind which also interested Bernard in 1874 was van Tieghem's translation of Julius Saachs' famous treatise on botany (*Geschichte der Botanik*). Bernard was conscious of defects in his botanical knowledge, not only when he tried to identify lichens for Mme. Raffalovich, but when his Museum lectures touched the physiology of plants. He wrote to van Tieghim:

> I have read and reread your Saachs. How many things this book has taught me which I did not know before and which interested me extremely! You have revealed an entirely new botany to me. If I had known all this some years ago, my researches would have been abridged and I should have turned them in quite another direction. But there is perhaps yet time and I am setting about it.

The new experimental approach of Saachs in plant biology naturally attracted Bernard and his work on the metabolism of plants was a source for the view of plant nutrition which Bernard had already dealt with in his Museum lectures. How much Bernard was influenced by Saachs' Darwinism in his summer lectures of 1874 on reproduction and nutrition at the embryonic stage does not appear. The lectures were not included in the *Phenomena,* as they did not bear directly on the unity of the animal and vegetable kingdoms.

Bernard wrote that during this summer he was preparing "three works" for publication. He probably referred to the volumes of his lectures edited with the help of Mathias Duval, which eventually appeared over 1875 to 1877. There were the usual dinners (in summer often requiring a journey by train or river boat to Saint-Germain, Saint-Cloud, Versailles, or Bougival) and an exhibition of pictures to which he accompanied Mme. Raffalovich. He was also busy in his laboratory, and in July invited young d'Arsonval to act as voluntary *préparateur* at the College of France. In August he was severely bitten on the left hand by an experimental animal.

When he went down to Saint-Julien (declining this year the meetings of the A.F.A.S. at Lille), he was inclined to rest. He submitted to being serenaded during the harvest festival but confessed to feeling more honored than enlivened by the attention. The letter written to his daughter Tony belongs to this summer and is the only evidence that he maintained any relationship with his estranged family. This curious letter reads more as if it were addressed to the child Tony than to the young woman who would have been twenty-seven in August, 1874:

> My dear Tony, I am sending you today a basket of pears; the ripest are on top, the less ripe underneath. You will put them in a cupboard: they will ripen in succession and be good to eat in a week or a fortnight from now. In a few days I will send you a basket of black and white grapes and some peaches from the orchard; for the ones on the espalier are all over.
>
> Your aunt Jenny and her children have come to spend a few days with me and have gone back to Pouilly. They send you their love and kisses. I saw Monsieur Chrétien

yesterday; he has lost his old Jeanne, whom perhaps you remember. He sends you his compliments.

It is very hot here, all the fruits are drying on the trees; the vintage will be better than last year, but it will still be a poor year.

I send you and your sister my best love. Your affectionate father,

Claude Bernard.

The level of communication here contrasts sharply with the letter to Mme. Raffalovich in the same week inviting her to visit him with her whole family "to pass a day or two together without boredom for you, I hope." Although Bernard could offer the attendance of Mlle. Mariette, two bedrooms and three beds, it was decided that the Raffaloviches would be more comfortable at the hotel *du Faucon* in Villefranche. Bernard was anxious that they should come early enough this time to see the vintage. The festivities when they arrived included a picnic and tasting the new wine. Sophie Raffalovich afterwards related that her father, who was no drinker, became quite intoxicated. Mme. Raffalovich was very upset and Bernard, explaining that it was because the wine was new, took her into the garden to look at the flowers until her husband had recovered. According to Sophie her father "never forgot the day when the scientist's wine had gone to his head."

Back in Paris in October Bernard was included in half-a-dozen dinner parties and taken twice to the theater. He gave a small dinner party himself in December and wrote a day or two later: "My cold which you saw at its dawn is now in its zenith. It is impossible for me to articulate a word or entertain an idea, my discomfort is so great. . . . I persist, nevertheless, in the plan of opening my course on Friday."

The lectures for 1875 were on the old subject of "Liquids of the Organism and Toxic Substances." An auditor of this course, Dr. E. Callemand, recorded the impression, "If Claude Bernard was a fine writer and philosopher, he was certainly no orator. . . . It was an informal talk interspersed with many experiments, an extension of the laboratory." Bernard's reputation as an indifferent lecturer thus pursued him to the very end. Even a listener inclined in his favor, Georges Barral, was obliged to admit that the lectures usually began lamely, although they became more forceful as Bernard warmed to his subject. An incurable diffidence appears to have prevented him from getting on a proper footing with an audience, for the published lectures, with many indications that they preserve the spoken word, are well organized. It is difficult to believe that anything which Bernard said could have lacked logical arrangement, which, as Renan pointed out, was conspicuously the basis of his written style. The criticism to which the lectures are most open is that they were habitually limited to the exposition of Bernard's own work. His references to the work of others, when they occur, are always governed by their relation to his own experiments. In consequence, the lectures do not always give a complete picture of the physiology of his time.

The volume which appeared in 1875 collected the courses of 1869-1870, with additions from his contemporary researches, under the title *Leçons sur les anesthésiques et sur l'asphyxie* (*Lectures on Anesthetics and Asphyxia*). It is important as a source for his work on carbon monoxide and for his theory of anesthesia. The prevailing view had been that anesthesia was merely an asphyxia. Bernard thought his experiments were best explained on the hypothesis that anesthetics produced a reversible coagulation of the constituents of the nerve cell, and also of other less sensitive tissues. In the case of the latter longer exposure or greater concentration of the anesthetic were required. In this connection he made the interesting discovery (an important contribution to general physiology) that plant as well as animal tissue is susceptible to anesthesia.

His general theory was not immediately accepted, because it was claimed that a much higher concentration of the anesthetizing agent was necessary to produce coagulation than merely to produce anesthesia, and that such coagulation was irreversible. Recent experiments have shown that, under proper conditions, a small concentration of anesthetic will produce coagulation in certain colloidal systems and even in living yeast cells, and that the process is perfectly reversible. Still more recent experimenters have again questioned the coagulation hypothesis, and the verdict remains inconclusive.

The Museum course opening in April, 1875, was devoted to a full statement of Bernard's general view of the nature of vital processes. He began with a painstaking historical review of the question from Pythagoras to Hegel, which bore witness to an advance from the amateurishness of his 1865 notebook. The bedrock of his position was still the scientific determinism defined in his *Introduction.* However, he had reflected on his view of causation (this appears also in the jottings of *Pensées*) and wished to substitute "the determined conditions of a phenomenon" for the old terms *secondary* or *immediate* cause.

> If we wish to attach to the word *cause* the sense of an origin of some sort, it cannot be applied to the natural phenomena which we observe, because in reality we are present at the origin of nothing; we observe only mutations, transformations of phenomena in determined conditions. Taken in a metaphysical sense, all causes escape

> us, by whatever name they are called, primary, secondary, or immediate.

The agitation into which Bernard worked himself while struggling to define "the conceptions to which continual meditation on the problems of physiology" had led him may be judged from a letter written to Mme. Raffalovich during July, 1875:

> Your letters carry a breath of fresh and fragrant air from the seashore into my dry parched life in Paris. I do not think that the void can be more terrible than this treadmill of forced labor to which one is bound in this free country of ours. I give up, I am losing my head, my sleep, and my health. Yesterday I spent the day in bed exhausted. Today I got up to give my lecture fasting; I admire my energy and persistence; it reminds me of the vanished years of my youth, . . . I expound my ideas on the properties of physical, chemical, and vital matter to everyone I meet; yesterday to Chevreul; today to Berthelot; tomorrow to someone else; and so on. You do not know to what you are exposing yourself in inviting me to stay with you; I am in a state to set forth all my physiological-philosophical theories, if I have not yet guessed the riddle. Let us hope I shall solve it soon.

Presently he began to navigate smoother nonphilosophical waters, as he developed the doctrine that the characteristics of life went back to the individual living cell: "The whole of life can only be the sum of its partial manifestations, grouped, linked together, displayed in variable order and degree. Complex vital manifestations are the result of the manifestations of the tissues, as a tune is the result of simple sounds."

As illustration of the susceptibility of a wide variety of living tissues to the same external stimulant he used his discovery that plants as well as animals are susceptible to anesthetics. He demonstrated that ether not only stops the beating of the frog's heart and the ciliary movement of the lining of the frog's esophagus, but also prevents the leaves of the sensitive plant from folding up when touched. Although his general theory of anesthesia has been questioned, his demonstration that plant as well an animal cells respond to anesthetizing agents remains uncontroverted.

According to Bernard, the complexity of vital phenomena was enough to distinguish them without assuming any difference in kind: "There is perhaps not a single chemical phenomenon in the organism which is carried out by the processes of the chemistry of the laboratory; in particular, there is no oxidation which is accomplished by the direct fixation of oxygen." He believed that the two aspects of vital phenomena, the processes in which the organism was broken down and destroyed in use and the processes by which it was nourished or regenerated were both dependent upon chemical agents peculiar to the living organism. Their uniqueness and peculiarity were explicable in the light of their complexity and their evolutionary history. Nature has been a chemist for a long time.

Concurrently with the preparation of these lectures Bernard was engaged upon an essay for the *Revue des deux mondes,* which under the title "Definition of Life" summarized much of their material. Here he carried the subject to the point reached above, that is, to the conclusion that vital phenomena exemplify a uniquely complex chemistry. He then added a discussion of the *propriété évolutive,* by which he meant the capacity of the germ to form from the material around it a living substance and endow it with "the chemical instability which becomes the cause of incessant vital movements," and to carry on this development until a life cycle has been completed. In the last Museum lecture he spoke of the egg cell as "the most potent and most marvellous of the agents of living chemistry."

His best attempt to define his own position of *physical vitalism,* midway between "the two schools which make vital phenomena something absolutely distinct from physicochemical phenomena or something competely identical with them" is found in the essay:

> In saying that life is the directive idea or the evolutive force of the living being, we express simply the idea of a unity in the succession of all the morphological and chemical changes accomplished by the germ from the beginning to the end of life. Our mind grasps this unity as a conception which is imposed upon it and explains it as a force; but the error consists in thinking that this metaphysical force is active in the manner of a physical force.

This statement is in accord with the interpretation already given to Bernard's account of the "directive idea" in his *Introduction.* The organism is *intelligible* to the scientist only as a "unity in the succession of all the morphological and chemical changes accomplished by the germ from the beginning to the end of life." This has common ground with the "interpretative idea" of Kantian idealism, with which Bernard's conception has been compared, but identification is prevented by Bernard's phrase that this conception is "imposed upon the mind." The Kantian idea rather imposes itself upon phenomena, when this idea interprets the world for mind. Bernard was in fact more at home with the seventeenth-century philosophers Descartes and Leibnitz than with the nineteenth-century idealism of Kant. From Leibnitz he quoted in this essay: "Everything goes on in souls as if there were no body, and everything goes on in the body as if there were no soul." And from Descartes: "One thinks in terms of metaphysics, but one lives and acts in terms of physics."

In August, as he was approaching the end of the ordeal of these lectures, he wrote:

> I must be off to my lecture. I hold forth on the vital properties, on their reality and the errors associated with them. I subtilize with courage, because I have a conviction of being in the right; but it is not *fun*. I am looking for my definitive formula. I catch a glimpse of it, I feel it. Often I think that I have grasped it, then it eludes me. Nevertheless I do not doubt that in the end I shall master it.

In another letter of this month he wrestled with his later view of causality. "Events or facts follow one another, are involved and mingled together according to a law which merely permits them to exist." He saw an illustration of this in an academic committee meeting where the decision reached did not seem to him to follow logically from the view of any particular person but was "the expression of the mass mind"—a phrase which Bernard attributed to Edgar Allan Poe, surprising us with his passing acquaintance with the American poet. That it was merely a passing acquaintance would follow from Barral's testimony that Bernard was not in general attracted to poetry.

Between the meetings of the A.F.A.S. at Nantes and his arrival at Saint-Julien Bernard sandwiched a visit of a few days to the seashore at Trouville with the Raffaloviches. In accepting the invitation, he warned Mme. Raffalovich that he meant to explain all his ideas to her "because your sensitive mind, with its understanding of language, will discover the defects or the weak points which will doubtless have eluded me."

In Saint-Julien he relaxed in his own way. Rising at half-past five in the morning, he snared migrating titlarks with a mirror and, with a charge of birdshot, "tumbled them into Mariette's casserole." For the rest of the day he was content to "meander about my vinegrowing functions" or amuse himself with the conversation of his three-year-old grand-niece. He detected the unfolding of another scientific mind: "Besides her merry disposition (she is never cross) and her roguish little face, she has a curiosity which makes her criticize and want to have explained everything she sees. She does not understand, among other things, why seeds have been put in grapes; she not only finds them useless, but does not like the way they feel on her tongue."

15

THE LAST EXPERIMENTS (1875–1878)

I have in mind matters which I want to finish conclusively. Letter to Mme. Raffalovich, 1877.

BEFORE HIS HOLIDAY, BEGUN WITH COUNTRY PLEASURES, WAS over, Bernard was spending part of his time in the improvised laboratory.

Until the publication of selections from Bernard's notebooks in Leon Delhoume's *De Claude Bernard à d'Arsonval* in 1939, there was no evidence that Pasteur was wrong in assuming that Bernard's experiments on fermentation had occupied him only during the last few months of 1877. But the dated entries in the series of notebooks show that his mind had been engaged upon the problem of the general nature of fermentation at intervals between 1851 and 1860, and that he had returned to it about 1872. The series of experiments on alcoholic fermentation undertaken during his Saint-Julien holiday in September and October, 1873, has already been mentioned. His earliest approaches derived from his interest in digestive ferments, such as pepsin or pancreatic juice, but his inquiries ranged over all the forms of fermenting action which he thought he recognized in blood and other liquids of the body. His directing idea was "to gather all fermentation, even alcoholic, under a single category."

The period during which the subject of fermentation was dropped coincides with the dozen years following Pasteur's statement of his theory of alcoholic fermentation in his memoir of 1860. Bernard then considered Pasteur's experimental evidence conclusive that the fermentation of grapes was dependent upon the presence of air-borne yeast cells.

It was not quite the same with the theory by which Pasteur had interpreted his experimental demonstrations. He not only maintained that there could be no fermentation without living yeast cells, but explained the process in terms of his theory of "life without air." He held that living yeast cells, unable to get oxygen from the air, split up the sugar molecule to obtain oxygen, thereby releasing alcohol and carbon dioxide. Fermentation was the result of the attempt of a living cell to get oxygen, not a simple chemical reaction between sugar and another chemical agent. Bernard's experiments of 1873 clearly questioned the hypothesis that fermentation depended upon the carrying on of life in the absence of free oxygen. He considered his results conclusive enough to be put into the formal record of his experimental notebook *R*.

The first two entries in notebook *S*, dated September 11, 1875, show a different approach to the problem. Bernard first announces a number of provisional hypotheses: that the soluble ferments are the only ferments, that ferments are the products of organic secretion, that it may not be true that alcoholic fermentation is hindered in a constantly aerated liquid, that fermentation fungi are parasites, that the production of alcohol precedes the formation of yeast.

In the experiments, solutions of yeast were washed several times through a filter, clearly in the hope of separating out a soluble ferment. He found that a filtered solution of yeast had lost the property of producing alcoholic fermentation, unless the yeast had begun to be active before the filtration began. The inactive filtered solution, he thought, could be activated or "nourished" if added to white of egg beaten up in water. If a sugar solution in a lively state of fermentation was filtered once so that most of the froth was retained by the filter, the residue continued its activity. If the same solution was put through a quadruple filter which retained the "molecular granulations," the residue was inactive or nearly so. He also examined the initial stage of alcoholic fermentation under his microscope. These were all preliminary studies for the isolation of a soluble ferment.

Not the least striking feature of these chemical adventures is the simplicity of the procedures. Temperature was regulated by putting a test tube in a cool room, in the sun on the window sill, or on the chimney piece in the kitchen.

In the middle of October Bernard returned to Paris, where he found d'Arsonval installed, since July, as *préparateur* in charge of the physical and technical aspects of researches at the College of France. D'Arsonval's medical course had two years still to run, so his duties were part time. Dastre, the other official *préparateur,* had charge of chemical researches and the keeping of records.

There was a heated debate in the Academy of Sciences that autumn over a suggestion Bernard had made in his Museum lectures of 1874 that the synthesis of starch in the plant leaf by the action of chlorophyl and the sun's rays had never been *experimentally* established. He had referred at that time to the practice of stripping away the leaves of beet-root plants, which did not seem to interfere with the sugar content of the mature beet-root. Viollette, dean of the Faculty of Sciences at Lille, at once planted two rows of beets, stripped the leaves of one row rigorously three times, and left the other row in full foliage. He got 2½ per cent advantage in sugar content of the total crop from the unstripped row. Bernard not only maintained that 2½ per cent was an insufficient difference to be decisive, but that Viollette's whole experiment was pointless because it used the statistical method. He pointed out that *some* of the stripped beets had shown a larger sugar content than *some* of the unstripped ones.

It seems incredible that Bernard should have taken this stand, but the statistical method was a *bête noire* with him. Although he denied that he had ever called into question the accepted theory of the formation of starch by the reduction of the carbonic acid of the air (for he insisted that he had only said that it had never been experimentally proved), he was attached to his view of the parallelism between nutritive processes in animals and plants and would have welcomed any evidence in its favor.

The discussion continued into December, Viollette being supported by a suggestion that the sugar content of individual beets of the same weight be compared, while Bernard insisted that this proof also would be merely statistical. He was finally permitted by the outraged agricultural chemists to have the last word, but it must have been merely out of deference.

In January of 1876 his winter colds began again, but he continued to accept invitations to dinner and the theater and also visited the studio of the sculptor Guillaume, who was eventually to do the statue of him for the terrace in front of the College of France. Guillaume profited by this opportunity for a life study of his subject and may have made a preliminary model of the statue, which represented Bernard at sixty-four. Paul Bert praised the likeness at the unveiling. He thought the artist had caught the seriousness and gentleness of Bernard's bearing, and also the "moment of pregnant surprise" in the midst of an experiment, when he became aware of "something new."

The *Leçons sur la chaleur animale* (*Lectures on Animal Heat*) appeared early in the year. They illustrate very well the way in which Bernard combined his early and his latest researches. He included experiments only recently carried out with the help of d'Arsonval's thermocouple needles to show that on stimulation of the chorda tympani the temperature of the submaxillary gland rose, while on stimulation of the sympathetic there was a fall in temperature. He saw this as additional proof of the hypothesis of "calorific and frigorific" nerves adopted twenty-five years earlier when he first observed the effects in the rabbit's ear following the cutting of the sympathetic nerve.

While he clung to this special interpretation of the increased blood flow, he was inclined to reject the designation of "trophic nerves" which had been proposed where the cutting of a nerve was followed by marked degenerative changes, *e.g.*, in the eye on cutting of the fifth nerve, as Magendie had observed. Bernard thought that these nerves had merely the function of vasodilation, and that it was unproven that nerves could modify the nutrition of a tissue independently of inducing changes in the blood supply. His point of view has been upheld. He also recorded experiments on the effects of various drugs, notably curare, on body temperature, and on the effects of high temperature on length of life.

There is no mention of lectures at the College of France for 1876 except in a letter of February 29:

> I gave my lecture yesterday with great difficulty; today I am half dead in body and in mind; this is a new edition

annotated and enlarged of my December cold. In consequence, I must give up. I shall not have the pleasure of dining with you tomorrow; I shall stay at home by the fire.

The weather in March was raw and foggy. Neuralgia and sciatica were added to his woes. At the end of the month the fireside had again become his "domain." He had no subject except his health in his notes to Mme. Raffalovich.

There were changes during 1876 in his staff of *préparateurs*. Dastre left for a chair at the Sorbonne which took all his time. D'Arsonval had not yet completed his medical degree but Bernard wished to make permanent his connection with the College of France. On July 6, 1876, he wrote to d'Arsonval's father, who was evidently disturbed at his son's proposal to abandon his professional medical career for one of scientific research:

> Sir, You express in your letter feelings of which your son Arsène has already informed me. I know that you were counting on him to be with you and to relieve you at the end of your medical career, and that it is a great sacrifice to be separated from him in order that he may enter scientific life in Paris. . . .
>
> Without doubt, scientific careers are not always so rapid in their material results as a professional career, properly so-called; but they have other pleasures which compensate. Besides, it is not a matter at this time of turning your son from his medical studies; quite the contrary. We have just finished my course at the College of France and your son will have his time almost free until December. I have urged him to pass his medical examination.
>
> Your son is still so young that he has time for reflection before making a definite decision, but I personally shall

> always encourage him in the direction of a scientific career, where I believe . . . that he has a fine future in reserve for him.

It was arranged that d'Arsonval should stay on, and for the last two years of Bernard's life he was the only *préparateur*. D'Arsonval completed his medical examinations according to plan and presented his thesis, dedicated to Bernard, in August, 1877. It was a completely independent piece of work on the role of the elasticity of the lung in the phenomena of circulation, largely an affair of blood-pressure measurement.

In the meantime the correspondence with Mme. Raffalovich had languished. There are only about a dozen notes in the first half of 1876, and in one of them Bernard ventured to reproach Mme. Raffalovich for having transferred her interest to "the camp of the littérateurs," perhaps since the publication of her novel at the end of 1875. He thought that "age creates emptiness around us." On July 9 (when, as the letter to the senior d'Arsonval indicates, Bernard was at a loose end after having just finished his course) a long letter complains that for the first time in their acquaintance Mme. Raffalovich had neglected to inform him of the day of her departure on holiday from Paris, so that he could call to make his adieus. He adds that he is so buried in his work that he can tell her nothing of what goes on in Paris. He mentions his experiments on the effects of anesthetics on plants, on which he was preparing a paper for the Society of Biology. Mme. Raffalovich must have replied for on July 27 he wrote again that a sheet of paper with the two words "Dear Madam" on it had been on his desk for a week while he tried to find time to answer the questions in her last letter. He said that his "publisher-editor" was "hanging on (his) heels" and that he was working desperately to finish the experiments in hand before the holidays. He was dining with the Princess Mathilde that evening, and was being urged to attend an international congress on hygiene in Brussels.

The lectures given at the Museum in the summer of 1876, eventually published in the first volume of the *Phenomena,* were the occasion of some of Bernard's most impressive pronouncements, particularly his final account of his conception of an internal environment, *le milieu intérieur*. When he first described this idea in *Liquids of the Organism* the emphasis was upon the protection furnished living cells by the nearly constant composition and temperature of the fluids which bathe them. In the *Phenomena* the thought centers on the maintenance by the living body of the constancy of its internal environment. A higher organism is so constituted that if its dynamic equilibrium is slightly upset in one direction, reactions take place which tend to restore the balance. The independence conferred on an organism by its internal environment sets it free to achieve its fullest development. The final formulation of Bernard's most important biological generalization was in these words:

> All the vital mechanisms, varied as they are, have only one object, that of preserving constant the conditions of life in the internal environment.

It was related to his later and more dynamic view of causation and supported his moral concept of freedom within limits.

Dastre was aware of the importance for Bernard's contribution to physiology of the views published in the second lecture of the first volume of the *Phenomena.* The wider public was at first more impressed by his concrete discoveries and his first English biographer, Sir Michael Foster, as late as 1899, was content merely to mention the *milieu intérieur.*

The concept has proved its value as a general point of departure for later scientific investigation. It thus served W. B. Cannon in his work on the role of the sympathetic nervous system in maintaining a constant internal equilibrium and J. S. Haldane in his comments on the philosophical implications of the view as well as in his research.

The studies of Professor Lawrence J. Henderson and Sir Joseph Barcroft represent more specific developments of Bernard's views, half a century after their formulation. Henderson illustrated the extreme complexity of the reactions maintaining organic equilibrium by his tabulation of the adjustments taking place simultaneously in six of the components of the blood which are linked to each other in a twenty-sided equilibrium.

Barcroft undertook to prove that the intellectual ascendancy of man may be considered a result of the fixity of his internal environment. He demonstrated that gross variations in the internal environment do not result so much in harmful disturbances of organs like the heart, muscles, or kidneys, as in damage to mental functions, *e.g.,* the ability to concentrate, to think logically, or pay attention. Recent studies in the physiology of aeronautics supply more evidence of this kind.

Recently also, the elaborate researches of Konrad Dobriner on the steroid hormones apply Bernard's concept of self-regulatory harmony to the medical problem: What causes cancer? Dobriner works on the hypothesis that an abnormal hormone situation leads to the development of cancer. He says: "The endocrine system . . . should be in harmony like a symphony orchestra. We want to prove that in cancer the orchestra is haywire."

In these Museum lectures some interest attaches also to

Bernard's treatment of fermentation, because it was at this time foremost in his experimental plans. It is, in fact, merely cautious and historical, noting the contributions of Berzelius, Liebig, Cagniard de Latour (to whom he gave the credit for the first observation, in 1836, that the yeast of alcoholic fermentation was formed of living cells), and Pasteur. He referred to the contemporary distinction between soluble and organized ferments, and listed the soluble ferments already isolated: diastase, pepsin, trypsin (credited to his German pupil, W. Kühne), and emulsin. Turning to the organized ferments, he said that "according to Pasteur," yeast causes alcoholic fermentation "when the ferment is deprived of air." He said that he was not attempting "a summary of the detailed state of our knowledge of these complex phenomena, but rather an indication of the place they should occupy in physiological investigation, reserving a later development to be supplemented by our personal researches." In the meantime, he defined fermentation as "a sort of parasitism which changes the environment in which these elementary beings live." In the light of the laboratory notebooks, the whole discussion can be read as a suspended judgment.

Bernard's relation with Georges Barral, the journalist, took on a certain importance when he gave this young man a remarkable token of gratitude for his companionship. On Monday, August 14, 1876, after Barral had accompanied him to the last lecture of his summer course, Bernard took Barral up to his flat and presented him with the manuscript of the play, *Arthur de Bretagne,* written forty-three years before. He said that he made the presentation in memory of his visit to Perpignan with the Barrals, and in recollection of an unnamed service which the elder Barral had done him in 1849. He gave Georges Barral permission to publish the play at his discretion, but not until at least five years after his own death, with the proviso that the original refusal of the play by Saint-Marc Girardin be mentioned. Barral remarked that on this occasion Bernard seemed quite vigorous and in good spirits because he was leaving Paris next day; the gesture was not made, as it were, in the shadow of the tomb.

Barral published *Arthur de Bretagne* in 1887 (waiting more than the five years) and two years later Bernard's elder daughter brought suit against him in behalf of her mother, her sister, and herself, because she considered a statement in the preface defamatory. Barral had said that Bernard's wife and daughters in 1869 left him in a "cruel state of abandonment." Mlle. Bernard won a judgment against Barral for 20,000 francs, together with a court order that all copies of the book be destroyed. Not content with the destruction of all the copies at the publisher's or in book stores, she or her mother kept watch for those which reappeared on the market. In consequence, the first edition is now a fairly expensive rarity. A second edition was published in 1943 and, in an abbreviated form, the play was produced for the first time over Radio-Paris, April 9, 1935.

Barral devoted a good deal of time to Bernard in the last two or three years of his life, and in particular made a habit of coming to the flat at 40, rue des Écoles, between nine and twelve on Sunday mornings to read aloud to him. Finding that poetry bored Bernard, Barral tried Diderot's *Physiological Notes,* which proved more successful. It occurred to Barral that the comments of a practicing physiologist upon this work of Diderot might be of journalistic interest. Bernard acquiesced, and notes were taken of the remarks with which he interrupted the reading. The projected commentary was never completed.

Before Bernard was free to begin his holiday in 1876, he

had his annual engagement with the A.F.A.S., this year at Clermont-Ferrand in Auvergne. He read a paper on "Sensitivity in the Animal and Vegetable Kingdoms," and took part in a discussion on the stripping of the foliage of beet-root plants, the truce in the Academy of Sciences apparently not being effective outside Paris. He also made after-dinner speeches, and went on the excursions to Vichy and Puy de Dome. In the case of the latter he declined the adventure of riding in the artillery wagons drawn by six horses provided for the journey. Instead he shared a cab with two of his colleagues and made the last part of the ascent on foot. The objective was the new meteorological observatory, which was being inaugurated on this occasion. Bernard was greatly impressed by the panorama, with its extinct craters and congealed lava streams, and also by the immense picnic of cold fowl and ham served to the scientists on the mountain top and washed down with the wine of Auvergne, described as "thin and flat" in comparison with the vintages of Beaujolais. He left early in his cab, but not in time to escape a drenching downpour on the way back, which was the beginning of another cold.

He was back in Saint-Julien before the end of August where his cold reconciled him at first to "doing absolutely nothing." He had a new metaphor: "My brain is an extinct crater: nothing smoulders, nothing comes to the surface, there is a dead calm." Presently he tried snaring titlarks again but the game was wary. He found it more interesting to supervise the labors of a crew of masons and carpenters who were doing repairs for him. His great-nephews came down with the measles. He dined at the "village chateau" which was less socially exalted than the chateau de Montmelas "on its rock," but unwaveringly royalist in its politics. At the end of September his old friend Lasègue came to spend three days with him.

In spite of these distractions he returned to his fermentation studies during September. He wanted to apply his new ideas on anesthetics to them. He made a preliminary entry in his notebook: "Many experiments already seem to indicate that yeast gives rise to a soluble alcoholic ferment; whence it should follow that there are in reality no organic or insoluble ferments."

He had already satisfied himself that anesthetics did not affect the action of soluble ferments. Could he use anesthesia to test the nature of alcoholic fermentation or, better, to analyze different stages in the process? He decided to make additional studies in the phenomena (especially coagulation of cell protoplasm) of anesthesia in the fungi of mildewed wheat.

As Pasteur was to recognize when he finally heard of these experiments, Bernard's starting point was the distinction he had made in the *Phenomena* (and elsewhere) between the processes of destruction and creation, the two complementary aspects of life. Creative processes were halted by anesthesia, but destructive or purely chemical processes were not interfered with. He thought he might learn a great deal if he could anesthetize an infusion of yeast and sugar but was balked by the technical difficulties of separating ether and alcohol.

He went back to his experiment of 1875, taking white of egg, allowing the normal sugar content to decompose, then beating it up in water, filtering it, and adding cane sugar to the filtrate. The result was "a slow fermentation" with formation of carbon dioxide. He tried the effect of a mild ether solution on this reaction and found that it continued. He was sure a stronger solution would stop it. His theory was that the white of egg provided a "diffuse protoplasm" which was the source of organizing ferments.

Their action initiated the process of fermentation which produced some alcohol, and the organized ferment, yeast, which in turn gave rise to an insoluble ferment and greatly accelerated production of alcohol. In other words, fermentation was a life cycle involving creation and destruction; the later, more rapid, stage of fermentation was the destructive phase. His whole investigation was at a very tentative and hypothetical stage.

Feeling restless and frustrated, Bernard dropped all this and went back to Paris a little earlier than usual, missing the visit of his old friend Paul Thénard, who arrived in Saint-Julien two days after his departure and, finding no one at home, chalked up his own name and the date on the doorway of the wineshed in lieu of a calling card. What was called "the pilgrimage to Saint-Julien" was often made by old friends and by "the disciples," former research associates, and *préparateurs* who had graduated into their own careers, even sometimes by total strangers who imagined they had an adequate excuse for a visit to a famous scientist. Bernard seems to have enjoyed doing the honors for his guests, displaying his view of the Saône valley from its best vantage points, and conducting tours of the vineyards and the cellar.

In an undated letter, preserved by Mme. Raffalovich with the letters of the early summer of 1876, Bernard wrote

> I began my course today and at the same time I put my shoulder to the wheel of the preparation of my grand treatise in three large volumes, of which I hope to begin publication forthwith. You will probably see me absorbed in it for the rest of my days, for they are now numbered and I can no longer be certain of completing my enterprises. . . . I expect soon to be rid of many adventitious occupations and regain possession of myself and my books, with activity in my researches if my health permits.

> I shall be forced to shut myself up next winter and completely give up society, if not my friends.

Until the publication by Delhoume in 1947 of a notebook and supplementary papers from the d'Arsonval collection under the title *Principles of Experimental Medicine,* it was customary to think of the *Experimental Pathology* of 1872 and the posthumous *Operative Physiology* of 1878 as the nearest Bernard came to carrying out his plan for a "grand treatise" on experimental medicine. These two volumes of lectures in fact do fulfill in a measure his promise "to regularize operative procedure" in physiology, the first half of his program of December, 1865.

The rest of that program, the exposition of the relation between experimental physiology and scientific medicine, is the theme developed in the notebook published by Delhoume. The central idea of the evolution of medicine through its prescientific, empirical, observational, and fully experimental stages[1] had been clear in Bernard's mind in 1865, and there are scraps of internal evidence to show that a good deal of the contents of the notebook was composed in the late sixties. It is likely, however, that the effort to fill in the existing broad sketch and bring the work to completion was made during 1876-1877. Two chapters (XIV and XV) appear in a form fuller than that of the notebook. These Delhoume found in loose sheets

[1] This arrangement of his subject in evolutionary historical stages is comparable to the evolutionary stages of positivist theory. Pierre Mauriac *(Nouvelles Rencontres, Le Tourment de Claude Bernard,* Grasset, 1930, p. 173) holds that Bernard's philosophical views had no originality or importance and that he "jealously concealed his positivistic affiliation." The authors hold that Bernard consciously rejected positivism.

along with a preface, dated February, 1877, in which Bernard reverts to the long gestation of his project. He adds that nothing had come in the meantime from foreign laboratories, assumed to be better equipped than his own, to supersede the work he had planned.

It is likely that the material published by Delhoume, incompletely developed as it is, gives a good idea of what the finished work would have been. There is little which is absolutely new except the dogmatic scheme of arrangement. The old illustrative stories, familiar from the published lectures and the *Report,* reappear, and the doctrine of the *Introduction* is restated. There is a fuller treatment of the statistical method in medicine, and Bernard's rejection of it is systematically justified by relating it to the empirical (or pre-experimental) phase of the evolution of science. There is a reference to Pasteur in the 1877 preface expressing Bernard's critical attitude toward him at that time: "So, Pasteur follows his ideas and wants to submit the facts to them, while I follow the facts and try to bring ideas out of them without violence and of their own accord."

The idea that Bernard values the victories of his own science only as contributory to a reformed *medicine* dominates all that he has written here.

There are indications that Bernard in his later years disliked the direct labor of writing. He expressed this in 1873:

> I am not out of my preface or rather I cannot get into it. I prefer experimenting. I notice in this connection that one takes one's habits of mind from the nature of the thing one studies and the way in which one studies them. The experimenter cannot think without being stimulated by an experiment, by a natural fact which presents itself to him; the mind grows dull and always needs an exterior excitant. The thinker properly so-called takes his initia-

tive in himself, and facts sometimes annoy and embarrass him. But all these reflections do not write my preface.

In spite of the modest limitation of his capacities here implied, Bernard covered reams of paper with his fine sloping handwriting in order to give his views a precise and personal formulation. However, he liked the cooperation of an editor in preparing a book for the press. Dastre assisted him in assembling the material for the first volume of the *Phenomena,* placed in the publisher's hands during 1877. The *Leçons sur le diabète et la glycogenèse animale* (*Lectures on Diabetes and Animal Glycogenesis*) appeared in the same year, under the editorship of Duval, whose help in coordinating the material of lectures and supplementary researches is acknowledged in the preface.

A detail, illustrating how Bernard's later activities complemented earlier work, occurs in his account in the *Diabetes* of the breaking down of cane sugar in the small intestine. In 1843 he had shown how gastric juice converts cane sugar into glucose and fructose, which we now consider to be completely accounted for by the hydrochloric acid present. He now showed that in the intestine there was a true ferment (invertase), which accomplished the same end. As a matter of fact, in the living body the hydrolysis of cane sugar is accomplished almost entirely by the ferment of the intestinal juice and to a very small degree by the acid of gastric juice.

Another point made in these lectures concerns the role of glycogen in the muscles. In the late fifties Bernard had shown that the living muscle consumes oxygen at rest as well as during contraction, active contraction causing increase of consumption. At the same time muscle glycogen undergoes a kind of fermentation which changes it to lactic acid. The detail which Bernard dealt with in the *Diabetes* was the relationship between rigor mortis and the formation of lactic acid in muscle. Under ordinary conditions, when a muscle dies it stiffens and becomes acid through the change of glycogen into lactic acid. When, however, an animal whose muscles contain no glycogen, *e.g.,* after long fasting, is killed, it passes into rigor mortis, but the muscle is found to be alkaline, not acid. The significance of Bernard's observation that rigor mortis can occur without the formation of lactic acid became evident after a lapse of some fifty years, when it was shown that muscular contraction also can take place without the formation of lactic acid and with little or no glycogen present. We now believe that glycogen and lactic acid are concerned only with recovery from muscle contraction, not with the actual contractile process itself.

The letters to Mme. Raffalovich in 1877 were fewer and briefer than for any other year. They were almost all concerned with his increasing nervous fatigue and sudden attacks of neuralgic pain. "One day I am better, the next I am worse, and it will probably go on like that until I no longer feel anything at all." He gave his lectures nevertheless. "I pursue my career in the midst of my alternating miseries, as a star continues on its orbit oblivious of bad weather." He confessed to losing his temper in public at the Academy of Sciences at the end of July. A friend (perhaps Pasteur) remonstrated with him: "There is surely something wrong; one would think you had a grudge against the whole world and were desperate at finding no one to take it out on." He was even obliged to apologize to Mme. Raffalovich:

> If I had a moment of irritability or exuberance, I ask your pardon. It was not for the reason which you doubtless suppose. I feel that I have some explanations to give you myself on this subject. I shall come to see you on

Sunday evening between eight and nine on my way to make my adieus to the Princess, your neighbor.

Relations were at once restored. Bernard wrote a few days later to say that he was sitting for his portrait. Nevertheless, for the first time, no letters were written from Saint-Julien during the vintage of 1877.

The full record of Saint-Julien for September and October is in his notebook on fermentation. He first wrote out a résumé of all his results in 1873 and 1875, with a view to repeating the crucial experiments under better controlled conditions. Before he left Paris he had been at pains to consult Berthelot and Pasteur about the best means of testing for small quantities of alcohol. Pasteur was to remember this a year later when some of Bernard's notes on fermentation were made public under circumstances embarrassing to him. It was, in fact, Pasteur's technique which Bernard used. The apparatus was a bent glass tube, the short arm of the angle consisting of a bulb in which the liquid to be tested could be heated. Very small quantities of alcohol (according to Pasteur) could be detected from the shape of the drops which formed on the cool walls of the long open arm of the tube. This simple instrument is repeatedly referred to in Bernard's notes as the *alcooscope* or *alcooloscope.*

The principal conclusions already arrived at by Bernard were that the fermentation of grape juice demanded the presence of air, that the formation of yeast was independent of germs from the air, and that the process of fermentation involved two periods, one of decomposition during absence of air and the other of organic creation depending upon access of air. He thought he had shown that alcohol and carbon dioxide were formed in small quantity in grape juice kept free from contact with air, and he added, with an interrogation mark: "Without yeast?" He summed up: "Fermentation includes two things: an insoluble ferment, a soluble ferment. The soluble ferment gives rise to the insoluble ferment and the latter to the former, and so on. . . ."

The first set of experiments aimed at testing, with careful controls, whether the fermentation of grape juice demanded the presence of air. He concluded that clear, perfectly fresh grape juice, hermetically sealed, did not ferment or decompose, but remained clear with no increase of alcoholic content. The same juice, after having been kept for some time, fermented very quickly on exposure to air.

The next series of experiments established the presence of a small quantity of alcohol in the fresh juice of a number of ripe fruits: grapes, peaches, pears, figs, medlars, overripe apples. He concluded that alcohol was a normal product of the ripening of fruit.

In October he drew up new plans, emphasizing his idea of the two periods of the fermentation cycle, and making a forecast that yeast would be found to be the source of a soluble alcoholic ferment. On October 6 he recorded what he called the "discovery" that alcohol was formed by the action of potassium hydroxide on glucose. This was the result of an accidental observation when he was trying to clear grape juice of acetic acid which he had found to be a cause of error in determinations for alcohol.

A few loose sheets for October 19, 20, and 22, which seem to have fallen out of the bundle of records, were eventually published at the instigation of Berthelot after Bernard's death. These notes were day-to-day experimental jottings and the only material at Pasteur's disposal when he attempted to estimate Bernard's work. They are greatly illuminated by the more orderly presentation in the notebooks.

After his return to Paris, Bernard did not lay aside his fermentation experiments as in previous years, but took d'Arsonval into his confidence about the work done at Saint-Julien and instructed him to make tests for alcohol in a number of samples brought to Paris. D'Arsonval described the routine of 1877 in the preface to the posthumously published *Pensées.* When the completion of his medical studies placed him more at Bernard's disposal, the two began to spend all day in the laboratory, a midday meal being brought across by Mariette so that their activities would not be interrupted. In the evening d'Arsonval would often accompany Bernard to the flat, and they would go over the day's work and compile the results from rough notes.

Bernard received his visitors in the small private room arranged for his special use on the first floor, above the laboratory. During November and December he remarked in confidence to several visitors, including Berthelot, Armand Moreau, Paul Bert, and Dastre, that he was engaged on a new series of researches on alcoholic fermentation and he thought his findings would modify the accepted theory. He made no mention of the matter to Pasteur, which may have been the result of delicacy, since Pasteur's view was under attack. Pasteur, however, later felt that Bernard had not behaved with the openness which their friendship should have warranted.

Bernard was reported to have remarked, on various occasions: "Pasteur's experiments are exact, but he has seen only one side of the question"; or "There is no life without air. . . . You shall see in my course; I did some good things in the holidays"; or "Pasteur has seen only one side of the question. The formation of alcohol is a very general phenomenon. The vitality of cells has no place in fermentation. I do not believe in it."

The results of Bernard's activities at the end of 1877 are

contained in notebook *T*. He tested his *alcooloscope* with solutions of alcohol in varying concentration, evidently with a view to making his observations more quantitative. He seems to have had no suspicion that his method was hopelessly crude. At all events it had been recommended by Pasteur. He tried a number of variations of his potassium hydroxide experiment. It is perhaps not possible to say that Bernard *could not* have obtained alcohol in this way, but his crude test for alcohol could certainly not be held to have established the finding. He was at some pains to describe the best procedure:

> It has occurred to me to observe that the best conditions for producing alcohol by means of KOH were to throw the caustic potash in bits in a hot concentrated (or unconcentrated) solution of glucose. If the potassium is previously dissolved or if the reaction is carried out at a low temperature, the quantity of alcohol formed seemed to me smaller. It seems to be the brusque action of the caustic potash on the sugar which produces a reaction in which water is taken from the sugar.

He also watched the process of fermentation using a filtered infusion of dry yeast and was convinced that alcohol was formed before fresh yeast was produced. He then either made (or perhaps only planned) a wide range of experiments with various grains (wheat, barley, hay), beans, apples and pears, seeds (mustard, cress, flax), chestnuts, potatoes—all with a view to the production of alcohol without yeast. He had a new idea: that soluble ferments were chemical ferments, and insoluble ferments physical ferments. He therefore planned, and in a few cases executed, experiments using dialysers (rubber bladders, porous dishes, organic membranes). The form which he hoped to give his proof that alcohol was formed without yeast is indicated in a summary drawn up in mid-December:

> Grapes, overripe fruits form alcohol without air, but when they are crushed and water is added bringing them into contact with air, alcohol continues to form, but yeast appears, and it acts in the production of alcohol.
>
> A means must therefore be found of preventing the formation of yeast without preventing the formation of alcohol.

On December 20 he drew up a list of conclusions, of which the most general were:

> 1. I have made a great number of exploratory experiments which have revealed to me a great number of new facts which all indicate the formation of alcohol in a wide range of circumstances without the presence of yeast.
>
> 2. Some facts seems of a nature to explain the mechanism of this formation of alcohol which has moreover nothing to do with vitality. These assumed vital influences which the chemists invoke must be banished from physiology.

It was the attitude implied in such statements as the last which led to the supposition in some quarters that Bernard's experiments were, like the successful ones of Eduard Büchner twenty years later, aimed directly at the separation from yeast cells of a soluble ferment. The publication of his experimental notes has shown how essentially different was his approach to the problem.

In spite of his industry in the laboratory, Bernard's health was miserable all through the autumn of 1877. He vacillated between saying: "My illness is quite accidental and psychological," and admitting that he was defeated:

> I was seized by a sciatic pain this morning which increased to such violence that it is impossible for me to walk and come to dinner with you. The pain is so intense as to be unendurable.

He opened his winter lectures in December as usual, but gave only six. He wrote to Mme. Raffalovich: "I have suspended my course for a month. Heaven grant that it will be enough." Georges Barral, with his journalist's touch, provides a funereal anecdote. He accompanied Bernard across the street to his last lecture at the College of France, and they had to wait a moment for a passing funeral. Bernard pointed to a priest in one of the carriages and remarked that he hoped he would have no such companion on his way to the grave. Barral mentioned that a Carmelite had attended Bernard's lectures. "Yes," said Bernard, "but his being there upsets me whenever I have to draw a philosophical conclusion in my lecture, for I should not like to offend him."

On New Year's day, 1878, Bernard attempted to make some of his customary calls and catching cold, developed a severe inflammation of the kidneys. A cystic examination was made by Dr. Gosselin and Dr. Felix Guyon. When Pasteur complained to Bernard that his theory of the microbe origin of disease was slow in gaining recognition among practitioners, Bernard mentioned this examination, remarking, with a smile, that he had noticed that of his two doctors the senior washed his hands and instruments *after,* and the junior *before* the examination. Apparently both schools believed in washing only in moderation.

At first Bernard was confined to his room, although not to his bed. His favored sitting room, even when he was well, was also his bedroom. Its furniture included the bed, hung with blue damask curtains, a table heaped with books, journals, and papers in front of the fireplace, his bookcases and armoire, and a large armchair.

He talked to his visitors about his plans for revising the theory of fermentation and using this material in his Museum lectures in the spring. He added, according to d'Arsonval, that he would like first to discuss all his ideas with Pasteur. On January 6 he did not try to leave his bed and soon grew too weak even to want to read his letters, which were read aloud to him by d'Arsonval, who, with Paul Bert and Mariette, assumed responsibility for the invalid.

When he grew worse, Paul Bert sent word to Bernard's sister, Mme. Cantin, and to his elder daughter. Bernard himself wrote to Mme. Raffalovich an undated and nearly illegible note: "Dear madame, ever since the first of the year I have been overtaken by a frightful attack of abdominal rheumatism. I suffer horribly. I can see absolutely no one. It is as much as I can do to write these few words." At first Mme. Raffalovich made her inquiries through d'Arsonval. She evidently commented on the painful character of the illness, for d'Arsonval wrote to her that Bernard had said: "Nature is sometimes very stupid; of what use is all this pain? It is useless for you or for me. I don't complain of suffering, I only complain that this suffering is of no use to anyone."

When recovery seemed unlikely, d'Arsonval made tentative efforts to learn what Bernard wished done about his last researches. It was too late. Bernard could only say: "It is all in my head, but I am too tired to explain it to you." He added: "Too bad, last summer I did some good work. . . . It would have been nice to have finished it." Apparently he gave no directions about his last entries in his notebooks, but made a recommendation to his heirs that all his unpublished works be entrusted to d'Arsonval.

In February Mme. Raffalovich and her daugher Sophie

began to share the nursing. They spent the afternoons with Bernard, leaving at about six in the evening. Bert, d'Arsonval, and Dastre took turns in staying up for the night. The Raffaloviches were very discreet: "When visitors arrived, we withdrew."

Two days before Bernard died, he was visited by Père Didon, the Dominican who had attended his lectures and who was on his way to becoming a celebrated publicist for the Roman Catholic Church. The two had a long interview during which they discussed Bernard's attitude to formal religion. Bernard said that he was not a materialist or a positivist (he had said this in his published works many times) and that he would be sorry if his exposition of scientific principles had done anything to disturb or destroy religious faith. Père Didon reassured him: "Your science does not lead away from God, but toward him. I know that from my own experience." Bernard remarked that his philosophical views had been somewhat revised since he wrote the book by which he was best known outside of scientific circles, the *Introduction*. He spoke of it in a deprecating way as "a book of my youth." He said that he had known suffering, both in body and mind, in his lifetime, and that he felt he had "done what he could."

His sister had arrived from the country, and a brother-in-law, representing his wife's family, came to see him on the morning of February 9. This relative, M. Saint-Amand, testified that Bernard was in complete possession of his faculties, discussed the disposition of his estate, and even mentioned 6,000 francs in a drawer in his desk as being "enough for the funeral." During the day his daughter Tony came to the apartment, but did not go into her father's room. Sophie Raffalovich said that she and her mother listened to Tony's footsteps as she walked up and down in an adjoining room and "the sound smote us to the heart."

In the evening Bernard's sister, without consulting his scientific friends, summoned the Curé of Saint-Séverin, the Abbé Castelnau, who received Bernard's confession and administered extreme unction. Paul Bert, d'Arsonval, and other friends, were in a room adjoining the sick room, and when the Abbé, after performing the last rites, came into the room wearing his surplice, it was felt that he meant to suggest a triumph of the church over scientific irreligion. Paul Bert was particularly indignant and insisted that Bernard must have been already unconscious when the priest was summoned. Père Didon later testified to his conviction that Bernard "died in the faith of his mother and as she who had loved him so much had hoped that he would die." Mme. Raffalovich and Sophie were equally convinced that Bernard did not undergo anything like a religious conversion at the end of his life "without telling his friends."

The last words recorded by tradition as having been spoken by Bernard related to an old traveling rug which he had noticed being placed over his feet: "This time it will serve me for the voyage from which there is no return, the voyage of eternity." Family tradition held that his daughter Tony came to him while he was still living, but d'Arsonval alone speaks of having been with him at the very end, at half-past nine in the evening, Sunday, February 10, 1878. At the request of Mme. Raffalovich a death mask was made, a copy of which has been preserved by the family of Paul Bert.

16

RECOLLECTIONS AND IMPRESSIONS OF A GREAT SCIENTIST

Those who, like myself, have spent long hours in the intimacy of this revered master will never forget those affectionate conversations in which he, so to speak, demonstrated before us the workings of his genius. Funeral address of Armand Moreau, February 16, 1878.

CLAUDE BERNARD'S GREAT SCIENTIFIC PRESTIGE WAS RECOGnized in a dramatic way when the Chamber of Deputies voted him a state funeral, the first such honor to a scientist. On Saturday, February 16, the ceremony began at the Church of Saint-Sulpice, and after a long cortège through the streets of Paris, ended in the cemetery of Père Lachaise. The novelist Flaubert, who saw the procession, was deeply impressed by the demeanor of the crowds. "It was religious and very beautiful," he said.[1]

[1] The comment comes from Flaubert's letter to Mme. Roger des Genettes, March 1, 1878: "Well! And the death of the Pope! There is an event which produced little stir! The Church no longer has her old position, and the Pope is no longer Saint Peter. It is a small body of laymen which now constitutes the true church. The Academy of Sciences is the reverend council and the disappearance of a man like Claude Bernard is more to be reckoned with than that of an old gentleman like Pius IX. The crowd was perfectly conscious of this at Bernard's funeral. I was there. It was religious and very beautiful."

None of the funeral addresses[2] touched on the question whether Bernard would have countenanced the religious part of the funeral ceremony, but the matter was at once brought up in the scientific press. This was done not by Bernard's close associates, but by Georges Barral, who was not a scientist, and by J. L. de Lanessan, who was not well enough acquainted with Bernard's published work to know that he would have been no more willing to be described as a materialist or positivist than as an orthodox Roman Catholic. Partisans are often eager to see others in their own image. However, Émile Littré, official interpreter of positivism, soon took occasion in the *Revue de philosophie positive* to define Bernard's shortcomings as a positivist. In the following year the strict materialists also disclaimed him publicly in their *Pensée nouvelle.*

Another and more interesting controversy arose within six months of Bernard's death over the significance of his interrupted researches on fermentation. Plans had been made at once to complete the publication of work about which his designs were known. The first volume of his work on general physiology, the *Phenomena,* appeared within two weeks of his death. It carried a note that the proofs had been read by Bernard himself (Pasteur intimated that it was done during the last holiday at Saint-Julien), and that the second volume would be prepared by Dastre. Duval was collecting a final volume of the lectures at the College of France under the title *Leçons de physiologie opératoire* (*Lectures on Operative Physiology*). D'Arsonval, after consultation with Bert and Dastre, undertook a search through Bernard's papers for records of the work on fermentation, and found, laid away in a drawer in the bedroom at 40, rue des Écoles, a bundle of

[2] Funeral addresses were delivered by E. F. A. Vulpian in behalf of the Academy of Sciences, Paul Bert for the Sorbonne, and Armand Moreau for the Academy of Medicine.

loose sheets containing notes of experiments done at Saint-Julien in 1877. Curiously, the search was not thorough enough to reveal the entries in the notebooks *R, S,* and *T,* where the results had been reduced to better order and where the work before 1877 and what was done in Paris in October and November of that year was also included.

Berthelot had always been critical of Pasteur's theory of fermentation and he was an authority on the chemistry of the subject. Bert, Dastre, and d'Arsonval referred the question of the publication of the notes to him and continued Bernard's policy of saying nothing to Pasteur. Berthelot first recommended that d'Arsonval attempt to verify and carry further the experiments of the notes. When d'Arsonval met with no success, he approved publication of the manuscript in its existing state and consented to provide an explanatory preface. The notes appeared in the *Revue scientifique* for July 20 over Bernard's name. At noon that day, as he was going into the Academy of Medicine, Pasteur met Armand Moreau who, waving a copy of the *Revue,* asked if he had seen the article on fermentation by Bernard. Pasteur's natural surprise and chagrin was increased when he read the article.

He saw at once that a direct attack upon his theory of alcoholic fermentation was intended and was at first inclined to think that Berthelot was using material Bernard would never have considered publishing to undermine a view of which he (Berthelot) disapproved. Two days later Pasteur addressed the Academy of Sciences, pointing out the discrepancy between the fragmentary experimental records and the sweeping conclusions of the published notes. He referred to his friendly exchanges of conversation with Bernard at the end of 1877, in none of which had the new experiments been mentioned. He suggested that what seemed to be conclusions might only have been hypotheses for a reexamination of fermentation, since it was well known that Bernard often began an investigation by setting up hypotheses to be tested experimentally. He was assured, however, by d'Arsonval, Dastre, Bert, and Moreau that Bernard had made it clear in his confidences to them that he considered his experimental results adequate grounds for proposing a theory of fermentation different from Pasteur's, and that he had planned to make this the subject of his next course at the Museum.

Pasteur reluctantly decided that Bernard had deliberately excluded him from his confidence and that it was necessary to make a formal reply. With d'Arsonval he made a textual examination of the manuscript and was able to point out discrepancies between it and the published version, as well as the fact that it was unsigned, although certainly in Bernard's handwriting. He recalled that Bernard had become very farsighted of late years, and doubted whether his eyes had been equal to deciding when fermentation began in some of his samples. He also embarked upon a repetition of the experiments by which he had previously shown that grapes protected from air-borne yeast cells gave juice which did not ferment. In November he gave a demonstration before the Academy using clusters of grapes from a protected vine. Finally, in 1879, he published what he called a "refutation" of the posthumously published notes of Bernard. Retelling the whole story in detail, he conveyed with restraint the impression that not only Bernard's eyesight but his critical powers had failed him in 1877.

As a matter of fact, nothing was changed by this in the respective positions of the two men. Bernard had not sought to deny that air-borne yeast played a contributory part in the alcoholic fermentation of grapes. He was endeavoring to reduce fermentation to a chemical cause. Pasteur was quite justified in not accepting the available evidence as conclusive, but his experimental critique would have been more to the point if he had done what he said Berthelot should have done before publishing the notes,—undertaken experiments of his own along the lines indicated by Bernard. As it has turned out, both scientists have in a sense been vindicated and corrected by the passage of time. Yeast cells are still recognized as the source of the ferment which breaks down sugar into alcohol and carbon dioxide, although Bernard thought he had called this in question. On the other hand, in 1895, Eduard Büchner separated from yeast cells under pressure the soluble ferment which Pasteur refused to look for.

It is true that the extraction of a soluble ferment from yeast was only one of the ways in which Bernard envisaged the problem, and not the one to which he had devoted most attention in the notes available to Pasteur. However, Bernard's theoretical position was proved sound when Büchner isolated from yeast a chemical ferment which functions even in the absence of yeast cells. Although anaerobic micro-organisms exist, Pasteur's view that fermentation may be explained as life without air was replaced by Bernard's conception of fermentation as essentially a chemical rather than a biological process.

In the meantime the lectures of *Operative Physiology* had appeared at the end of 1878, and the second volume of the *Phenomena* was brought out to commemorate the first anniversary of Bernard's death, an occasion also marked by a mass at the church of Saint-Séverin performed at the instance of his family. Two years later an alphabetical index to the subject matter of his published works and a complete bibliography of these and his scientific papers was published, along with the address on

Bernard delivered by Renan on his reception into the French Academy, where he succeeded to Bernard's chair.

In February, 1886, a few days before the eighth anniversary of Bernard's death, a bronze statue of him, executed by Guillaume (the subscription initiated in the Society of Biology), was placed on the terrace in front of the College of France. This statue was removed for the metal during the German occupation of France in World War II, and was one of the first statues to be replaced by the French in stone, not with a replica of Guillaume's portrait, but by an original work by a modern sculptor. A marble bust of Bernard, with a basin for a foundation and a figure symbolic of youth, was set up in the square at Saint-Julien in 1885.

There are also the verbal memorials, in which men who had known Bernard left their impressions of his personality. In these there was unanimity about his devotion to science, the scope and value of his contributions, and the simplicity and kindness of his character. Pasteur said, even after the disappointment of being excluded from discussion of the experiments on fermentation, that Bernard "was one of the purest personifications of the scientist," and that no one would have been less inclined than he "to mingle extraneous considerations with the pursuit of truth." Berthelot, who had assisted Bernard in the chemistry of his work on the pancreas and liver, and been his colleague at the College of France, spoke of his "sincere zeal for science, his absolute freedom from false pretension, his unsleeping spirit of curiosity, and the surety of method which he applied to his investigations." He recalled also the early days when Bernard had been "the star and favorite" of the Society of Biology. Dr. Armand Moreau said that Bernard's pupils at his death lost "a guide and friend," and went on:

> He was open-minded, and at the same time sure of himself; he never seemed absorbed in his own views. . . . He never tried to produce any effect in speaking; and imagining other people to be like himself, he thought that the spirit of research which was his own inspiration would be enough to arouse their enthusiasm.

Both Paul Bert and d'Arsonval used the word "paternal" to describe Bernard's attitude to themselves. Paul Bert said that on his death-bed Bernard addressed his pupils as his "scientific family." He added that Bernard's affection was never indiscriminating; "although generous with advice and encouragement, he was as sternly critical of the work of his associates as of his own."

Renan, speaking on the occasion of his succession to Bernard's Academy chair, had the task of celebrating Bernard as a writer and of collecting as much as he could of the living tradition from the recollections of friends. He had access to the letters preserved by Mme. Raffalovich, as is proved by the quoted description of the Saône valley, a reference to Bernard's wish to complete the work on fermentation, and the outline of a scheme for the reformation of the human species, based on a theory of biological memory. Renan gave his praise to the critical spirit of Bernard as a scientist and thinker, whose life was "wholly devoted to truth." He spoke of the "absolute serenity" which arose from Bernard's confidence that his life had been well spent in the service of science.

Fifty years later, Pierre Mauriac, medical scientist and littérateur, questioned Renan's insight in calling Bernard serene. Mauriac was in revolt against the cult, founded by Berthelot and Paul Bert rather than Renan, which paid tribute to Bernard as the "high priest of determinism." Mauriac's religious views led him to represent Bernard as committed to a philosophy of science which thwarted an intuitive and religious temperament. The resulting portrait is as distorted as the one it was meant to replace, but Mauriac did service to Bernard's memory in showing how conventional and lifeless an image of "a great scientist and an unhappy man" was accepted by the extreme determinists.

Although the simplicity of Bernard's manner was so often spoken of—and we may well believe that he had the simplicity of an honest and intelligent man—his nature was not uncomplicated. He was always a little solitary and withdrawn, an easy prey to melancholy, in spite of his gift for inspiring friendship and affection. Science was his vocation and at the same time his refuge. He wrote to Mme. Raffalovich in 1875: "Science absorbs and consumes me; I ask no more if it helps me to forget."

BIBLIOGRAPHICAL REFERENCES

CHAPTER 1

BERNARD, CLAUDE: Rapport sur les Progrès et la Marche de la Physiologie Générale en France. Paris, Impr. Impériale, 1867.

BUTTERFIELD, H.: The Origins of Modern Science 1300-1800. London, G. Bell & Sons, 1949.

GENTY, GENEVIÈVE: Bichat, Médecin du Grand Hospice d'Humanité. Clermont (Oise), Thiron, 1943.

OLMSTED, J. M. D.: François Magendie. New York, Schuman's, 1944.

CHAPTER 2

BALLOFFET, J.: Silhouettes caladoises. Villefranche-en-Beaujolais, Guillermet, 1931.

BERNARD, CLAUDE: Arthur de Bretagne. Paris, Dentu, 1887.

DUPLAIN, L.: Notice historique sur Saint-Julien (Rhone) et sur Claude Bernard. Lyon, Audin, 1923.

FOSTER, M.: Claude Bernard. London, Unwin, 1899.

GENTY, M.: Claude Bernard. *Biogr. méd.,* September, 1932, pp. 129-144; October, 1932, pp. 145-160.

——: Claude Bernard. *Progrès méd.,* Suppl. 2, 1928, pp. 9-16.

GODART, J.: Les reliques de Claude Bernard à Saint-Julien, pp. 27-53. Villefranche-en-Beaujolais, Guillermet, 1936.

LYONNET, B.: Quatre lettres intimes de Claude Bernard, jeune étudiant. *Lyon médical,* 163, 249, 1939.

MILLET, RAYMOND: Claude Bernard, ou L'Aventure Scientifique. Paris, Nouvelle France, 1946.

MONDOR, HENRI: Claude Bernard. In: Grands Médecins Presque Tous, pp. 304-345. Paris, Corréa, 1943.

MONOD, G., AND THYSS-MONOD.: La vie de Claude Bernard. *Revue du mois,* February 10, 1914.

OLMSTED, J. M. D.: Claude Bernard, Physiologist. New York, Harper, 1938.

———: Claude Bernard as a Dramatist. *Ann. Med. Hist.* n.s. 7: 253-260, 1935.

RENAN, E.; Claude Bernard. Discours prononcé le jour de sa reception à l'Académie française, le 3 avril, 1879. L'Oeuvre de Claude Bernard, pp. 3-37. Paris, Baillière, 1881.

ROSTAND, JEAN: Claude Bernard. In: Hommes de Vérité, pp. 53-123. Paris, Stock, 1942.

VAN TIEGHEM, P.: Notice sur la vie et les travaux de Claude Bernard. *Mém. Acad. d. Sc.,* 52: i-xlii, 1914.

CHAPTER 3

BERNARD, CLAUDE: Recherches anatomiques et physiologiques sur la corde du tympan. *Ann. méd. psychol.,* 1: 408-439, 1843.

———: Du suc gastrique et de son rôle dans la nutrition. Thèse pour le doctorat en médecine. Paris, Rignoux, 1843.

———: Lettres Beaujolaises. Villefranche-en-Beaujolais, Cuvier, 1950.

MAGENDIE, F.: Leçons sur les fonctions et les maladies du système nerveux, professés au Collège de France. Paris, Ébrard, 1839.

CHAPTER 4

BERNARD, CLAUDE: Recherches expérimentales sur les fonctions du nerf spinal, ou accessoire de Willis. *Arch. gén. de méd.*, 4: 397-424; 5: 51-96, 1844.

———: Des matières colorantes chez l'homme. Thèse présentée et soutenue à la faculté de médecine de Paris. Concours pour l'agrégation. Paris, 1844.

CHAPTER 5

BERNARD, CLAUDE: Des différences que présentent les phénomènes de la digestion et de la nutrition chez les animaux herbivores et carnivores. *Comp. rend. Acad. d. Sc.*, 22: 534-537, 1846.

———: Du suc pancréatique et de son rôle dans les phénomènes de la digestion. *Mém. Soc. de biol.*, 1: 99-115, 1849.

———: Mémoire sur le pancréas. Paris, Baillière, 1856.

———: Introduction à l'étude de la médecine expérimentale. Paris, Baillière, 1865. *v.* Part III, Chapter I, pp. 267-269 (Eng. trans., pp. 151-155).

———: Recherches sur les causes qui peuvent faire varier l'intensité de la sensibilité récurrente. *Comp. rend. Acad. d. Sc.*, 25: 104, 106, 1847.

———: Leçons sur lequides de l'organisme. Vol. II, pp. 387-393.

CHAPTER 6

BERNARD, CLAUDE: De la présence du sucre dans le foie. (With Barreswill.) *Comp. rend. Acad. d. Sc.*, 27: 514-515, 1848.

———: Influences de la section de pédoncles cérébelleux sur la composition de l'urine. *Mém. Soc. de biol.*, 1 (C.R.): 14, 1849.

——: De l'origine du sucre dans l'économie animale. *Mém. Soc. de biol.*, 1: 121-133, 1849.

——: Sur une nouvelle fonction du foie chez l'homme et chez les animaux. Prix de physiologie expérimentale pour 1851. *Comp. rend. Acad. d. Sc.*, 31: 371-374.

——: Recherches sur une nouvelle fonction du foie. Thèse soutenue le 17 mars, 1853, pour obtenir le grade de docteur ès sciences naturelles. Paris, Baillière.

BURR, A. R.: Weir Mitchell, His Life and Letters. New York, Duffield, 1930.

HALDANE, J. S.: John Scott Burdon-Sanderson. *Proc. Roy. Soc.*, B 79: 14, 1907.

CHAPTER 7

BERNARD, CLAUDE: Le curare. In: La science expérimentale, pp. 237-315. Paris, Baillière, 1878.

MCINTYRE, A. R.: Curare, Its History, Nature, and Clinical Use. Chicago, Univ. Press, 1947.

CHAPTER 8

BERNARD, CLAUDE: De l'influence du système nerveux grand sympathique sur la chaleur animale. *Comp. rend. Acad. d. Sc.*, 34: 472-475, 1852.

——: Recherches expérimentales sur le grand sympathique et spécialement sur l'influence que la section de ce nerf exerce sur la chaleur animale. *Mém. Soc. de biol.*, 5: 77-107, 1853.

——: Sur le mécanisme de la formation du sucre dans le foie. *Comp. rend. Acad. d. Sc.*, 41: 461, 1855.

——: Introduction à l'étude de la médecine expérimentale, pp. 286-295.

——: Notes of M. Bernard's Lectures on the Blood (Taken by W. F. Atlee). Philadelphia, Lippincott, Grambo, 1854.

——: Leçons de physiologie expérimentale appliquée à la médecine. Paris, Baillière, 1855-1856, 2 vols.

BROWN-SÉQUARD, C. E.: *Phila. Med. Exam.,* August, 1852, p. 490.

CHAPTER 9

BERNARD, CLAUDE: Nouvelles recherches expérimentales sur les phénomènes glycogéniques du foie. *Mém. Soc. de biol.,* 9: 1-7, 1857.

——: Sur le mécanisme physiologique de la formation du sucre dans le foie. *Comp. rend. Acad. d. Sc.,* 44: 578-586, 1325-1331, 1857.

——: De l'influence de deux ordres de nerfs qui déterminent les variations de couleurs du sang veineux des organes glandulaires à l'état de fonction et à l'état de repos. *Comp. rend. Acad. d. Sc.,* 47: 393-400, 1858.

——: Leçons sur les effets des substances toxiques et médicamenteuses. Paris, Baillière, 1857.

——: Leçons sur la physiologie et la pathologie du système nerveux. Paris, Baillière, 1858, 2 vols.

——: Leçons sur les propriétés physiologiques et les altérations pathologiques des liquides de l'organisme. Paris, Baillière, 1859, 2 vols.

CHAPTER 10

BERNARD, CLAUDE: Du rôle des action réflexes paralysantes dans le phénomène des sécrétions. *J. anat. de Robin,* 1: 507-513, 1864.

——: Étude sur la physiologie du coeur. In: La science expérimentale, pp. 316-366.

DE GONCOURT, E.: Journal des Goncourts: Mémoires de la vie littéraire. Paris, Charpentier, 1890.

JOUSSET DE BELLESME, G. L.: Notes et souvenirs sur Claude Bernard. Nantes, 1882.

VALLERY-RADOT, R.: La vie de Pasteur. Paris, Flammarion, 1900.

CHAPTER II

BERNARD, CLAUDE: Introduction à l'étude de la médecine expérimentale. Paris, Baillière, 1865.

——: Du progrès dans les sciences physiologiques. (1865); Le problème de la physiologie générale. (1867). In: La science expérimentale, pp. 38-98; 99-148.

——: Philosophie, manuscrit inédit. Texte publié et présenté par Jacques Chevalier. Paris, Boivin, 1937.

——: Pensées: Notes détachés. Préface de M. le pr. d'Arsonval. Introduction et notes par le Dr. Leon Delhoume. Paris, Baillière, 1937.

——: Le cahier rouge. Introduction par le Dr. Leon Delhoume. Paris, Gallimard, 1942.

——: Principes de médecine expérimentale. Introduction et notes par le Dr. Leon Delhoume. Paris, Presses Universitaires de France, 1947.

BERGSON, HENRI: La philosophie de Claude Bernard. *Nouvelles litt.,* Nov. 17, 1928, p. 5. (Reprinted by E. Dhurout, in: Claude Bernard: Sa vie, son oeuvre, sa philosophie. Paris, Félix Alcan, 1939.)

LENZEN, V. F.: The Philosophy of Nature in the Light of Contemporary Physics. University of California publications in Philosophy, Vol. 5, pp. 25-48.

LAMY, PIERRE: Claude Bernard, le naturalisme et le positivisme. Paris, Félix Alcan, 1928. Claude Bernard et le matérialisme. Paris, Félix Alcan, 1939.

MARGENAU, HENRY: Conceptual Foundations of the Quantum Theory. *Science,* 113 (2926): 95-101, 1951.

OLMSTED, J. M. D.: The Contemplative Works of Claude Bernard. *Bull. Inst. Hist. Med.,* 3: 335-354, 1935.

PLANCK, MAX: Wissenschaftliche Selbstbiographie. Leipzig, Barth, 1948. (Eng. trans., New York, Philosophical Library, 1949).

RIESE, W.: Claude Bernard in the Light of Modern Science. *Bull. Inst. Hist. Med.,* 14: 281-294, 1943.

SERTILLANGES, A.D.: La philosophie de Claude Bernard. Paris, Aubier, 1943.

CHAPTER 12

BERNARD, CLAUDE: Discours de réception à l'Académie française. In: La science expérimentale, pp. 404-440.

———: Rapport sur un mémoire de M. E. Cyon. *Journ. anat.,* 5: 337-345, 1868.

DE MONZIE, ANATOLE: Les veuves abusives. Paris, Grasset, 1936.

ROSTAND, JEAN: *Op. cit. supra* (Ch. II), pp. 121-123.

CHAPTER 13

BERNARD, CLAUDE: Lettres de Claude Bernard, 1869-1878. Correspondance de Marie Raffalovich, t. xiii-xviii (48, 99, 92, 88 et 80 lettres autographes). Bibliothèque de l'Inst. Nat. de France, Mss. 2653-3658.

———: Lettres Beaujolaises, publiées et annotées par Justin Godart. Villefranche-en-Beaujolais, Cuvier, 1950.

CHAPTER 14

BERNARD, CLAUDE: Lettres.

———: Leçons sur les phénomènes de la vie communs aux animaux et aux végétaux. Paris, Baillière, 1878-1879. 2 vols.

———: Leçons sur les anesthésiques et sur l'asphyxie. Paris, Baillière, 1875.

CHAPTER 15

ALGLAVE, E.: Mort de Claude Bernard. *Rev. scient.,* Feb. 16, 1878, pp. 765-769.

BARRAL, GEORGES: Préface historique. In: Arthur de Bretagne. Paris, Dentu, 1887.

——: Claude Bernard. Verviers (Belgique), Gilon, 1889.

——: Diderot et la médecine. Un ouvrage projeté par Claude Bernard. *Chronique méd.*, 1900, pp. 126-128.

BERNARD, CLAUDE: Lettres.

——: Phénomènes.

——: Leçons sur la chaleur animale, sur les effets de la chaleur et sur la fièvre. Paris, Baillière, 1876.

——: Leçons sur le diabète et la glycogenèse animale. Paris, Baillière, 1877.

——: Définition de la vie. In: La science expérimentale, pp. 149-212.

DELHOUME, LEON: De Claude Bernard à d'Arsonval. Paris, Baillière, 1939.

DIDON, H.: Claude Bernard. *Revue de France,* 28: 1-20, 1878.

GODART, JUSTIN: La Mort de Claude Bernard. In: Lettres Beaujolaises, pp. 123-133.

CHAPTER 16

BARRAL, GEORGES: Correspondence. *Rev. internat. d. Sc.,* 1: 381, 1878.

BÉCLARD, J.: Éloge de Claude Bernard. *Bull. Acad. méd. de Paris,* 14: 714-739, 1885.

BERT, PAUL: Claude Bernard. In: La science expérimentale, pp. 15-35. Les travaux de Claude Bernard. In: L'Oeuvre de Claude Bernard, pp. 39-87.

BERT, P., M. BERTHELOT, FRÉMY, A. CHAUVEAU AND M. DASTRE: Inauguration de la statue de Claude Bernard. *Mém. Soc. de biol.,* 38 (C.R.): xi-xxiii, 1886.

DUVAL, M.; Claude Bernard. *Rev. de philos. positive,* 20: 424-444, 1878.

FAURE, J. L.: Claude Bernard. Paris, Crès, 1925.

FRANKLIN, A. W.: The Life and Works of Claude Bernard. (Wix Prize Essay, 1928.) *St. Barth. Hosp. J.,* 36: 2-8, 1928.

FULTON, J. F.: Claude Bernard and the Future of Medicine. *Canad. M. A. J.*, 27: 427-433, 1932.

GLEY, E.: L'Oeuvre pathologique de Claude Bernard et la biologie française. *Rev. scient.*, July 3, 1915, p. 257.

GODLEWSKI, H.: L'hommage de l'assemblée française de médecine générale à Claude Bernard. *Méd. gén. fr.*, 1: 424-425, 1934.

———: Discours. *Méd. gén. fr.*, 2: 16-17, 1935.

DE LANESSAN, J.: Obsèques de Claude Bernard. *Rev. internat. d. Sc.*, 1: 255, 1878.

LITTRÉ, E.: Du déterminisme de Claude Bernard. *Philos. positive*, 21: 5-11, 1878

MAURIAC, DR. PIERRE: Du scepticimse en médecine. In: Aux confins de la médecine. Paris, Grasset, 1926.

———: Claude Bernard, Ernest Renan et Marcelin Berthelot devant la science. *Rev. hebd.*, 11: 342-357, 1927.

———: Le tourment de Claude Bernard. In: Aux confins de la médecine: Nouvelles rencontres. Paris, Grasset, 1930.

———: La figure tourmentée de Claude Bernard. *Mercure de France*, 287: 278-288, 1938.

———: Claude Bernard d'après sa correspondance. *Progrès méd.*, October, 1950, pp. 500-501.

MOREAU, A.: Claude Bernard. Discours prononcé aux funerailles de Claude Bernard. L'Oeuvre de Claude Bernard, pp. 89-93.

PASTEUR, L.: Examen critique d'un écrit posthume de Claude Bernard sur fermentation. Paris, Gauthier-Villars, 1879.

POSTAND, JEAN: *Op. cit. supra* (Ch. II).

INDEX

D

M

N

O

P

Q

R

T

U

V

W

Y

Z